Beginning Reasoning and Reading

JOANNE CARLISLE

Educators Publishing Service, Inc.

Cambridge and Toronto

Educators Publishing Service, Inc.
31 Smith Place, Cambridge, MA 02138-1089

Printed in U.S.A.   ISBN 0-8388-3001-3

December 2000 Printing

Contents

BEGINNING
LEVEL

WORD
MEANING

Introduction

Words are units of meaning. Because they are the basis for communication, it can be helpful to learn about word meanings and how words are related to one another.

Some words have only one meaning. Some words have many meanings. For example, *light* and *lamp* share a meaning, but *light* has many other meanings.

lamp: something that gives off light or heat

some meanings of *light*:

- brightness
- a lamp, a lantern, a fixture
- daylight, dawn
- a source of fire

Words are related to each other in different ways. For example, notice how the word *kite* belongs in more than one group.

Toys	Things that Fly
kite	kite
yo-yo	helicopter
jump rope	bird
marbles	airplane

Sometimes different things can be alike. For example, what do these four things have in common?

apple, rose, stop sign, fire engine

_____

We can figure out the meaning of a word by looking at the words that surround it.

The word *bat* has several different meanings. What does it mean in sentence A? What does it mean in sentence B?

A. He picked up his mitt, his cap, and the *bat*.

B. The *bat* hunted for insects at night and slept all day.

UNIT 1
WORD
MEANING

Parts and Wholes

Can you tell parts of things from whole things?

A *cup* is a whole thing. The *handle* on the cup is a part of that cup.

Is a squirrel a **part** or a **whole**? _____ *whole* _____

Here are two words. One is a part, and one is the whole thing. Which one is the part?

squirrel—tail _____ *Part* _____

Directions: Look at each pair of words below. Is the underlined word a *part* or a *whole*? Write *part* or *whole* on the line. The first one has been done for you.

Example: <u>eraser</u>—pencil _____ part _____

1. <u>handle</u>—door _____ *Part* _____

2. number—<u>clock</u> _____ *Whole* _____

3. <u>cord</u>—lamp _____ *Part* _____

4. zipper—<u>jacket</u> _____ *whole* _____

5. <u>ink</u>—pen _____ *Part* _____

6. screen—<u>television</u> _____ *Whole* _____

7. <u>desk</u>—drawer _____ *whole* _____

8. bread—<u>crust</u> _____ *Part* _____

9. <u>string</u>—guitar _____ *Part* _____

10. tractor—<u>engine</u> _____ *Part* _____

UNIT 1
WORD MEANING

3

Parts and Wholes

Directions: Circle all the *parts* of a tree.

(branch)   (trunk)   (bark)

ground   bird's nest   (leaf)

saw   bush   (limb)

forest   grass   leg

(root)   (twig)   maple

Directions: Write down a *whole* to go with each part listed below.

1. crust _bread_   6. leg _body_

2. page _book_   7. wing _bird_

3. bone _Dinisor_   8. wheel _car_

4. door _not house_   9. handle _cup_

5. eye _head_   10. zipper _coat_

Directions: List as many *parts* of a car as you can think of.

weel   Door window
raidreaow   cupholder
roof Dashbord   ...
whisheelwiper

Classification

Directions: For each problem, find five things that all fit into the same group. Underline these five things. In the example, the underlined words are all parts of the body. *Shoe*, *donut*, and *handbag* are not body parts so they are not underlined.

Example: <u>toe</u>, shoe, <u>ear</u>, <u>stomach</u>, donut, <u>shoulder</u>, handbag, <u>lung</u>

1. <u>scarf</u>, <u>hat</u>, toothbrush, suitcase, <u>mittens</u>, <u>gloves</u>, <u>socks</u>, sled

2. <u>penny</u>, hat, <u>nickel</u>, <u>dime</u>, bank, <u>quarter</u>, newspaper, <u>half-dollar</u>

3. <u>cookie</u>, corn, <u>cake</u>, <u>pie</u>, blueberry, <u>cupcake</u>, noodle, <u>muffin</u>

4. chimney, <u>piano</u>, television, car, <u>guitar</u>, <u>trumpet</u>, <u>drum</u>, <u>violin</u>

5. <u>raft</u>, <u>rowboat</u>, train, <u>steamship</u>, <u>tugboat</u>, <u>canoe</u>, river, church

6. <u>marbles</u>, <u>blocks</u>, socks, <u>dolls</u>, wagons, shirts, trees, <u>teddy bears</u>

7. snake, <u>telephone</u>, <u>desk</u>, <u>chair</u>, <u>table</u>, <u>lamp</u>, truck, <u>bed</u>

8. <u>doctor</u>, dentist, <u>nurse</u>, medicine, <u>teacher</u>, <u>coach</u>, wheel, library

9. <u>plant</u>, stem, cheese, <u>flower</u>, hanger, <u>tree</u>, <u>ball</u>, <u>grass</u>

10. <u>fire</u>, test, <u>sand</u>, <u>ocean</u>, finger, <u>umbrella</u>, bathing suit, <u>suntan lotion</u>

✓ Classification

Directions: Put the words below into two lists—*birds* and *other animals*. Cross off each word as you put it in the correct group.

~~fox~~, ~~pigeon~~, ~~eagle~~, ~~squirrel~~, ~~elephant~~, ~~crow~~, ~~chickadee~~, ~~duck~~, ~~rat~~, ~~wolf~~, ~~robin~~, ~~giraffe~~, ~~sea gull~~, ~~hawk~~, ~~cow~~, ~~sheep~~

Birds	Other Animals
Pigeon	fox
eagle	squirrl
crow	elefant
chickadee	rat
duck	wolf
robin	giraff
seagull	cow
hauk	sheep

✓

Directions: Sort the things below into two groups—*fruits* and *vegetables*. Cross off each one as you put it in its group.

~~lemon~~, ~~cabbage~~, ~~pea~~, ~~apple~~, ~~pear~~, ~~grape~~, ~~bean~~, ~~watermelon~~, ~~carrot~~, ~~peach~~, ~~lettuce~~, ~~onion~~

Fruits	Vegetables
lemon	cabbege
apple	pea
pear	bean
grape	carott
watermelon	ledess
peach	onion

✓

✓ Classification

Directions: Put the words below into two lists—*people* and *places*. Cross off each one as you put it in the correct column.

~~nurse~~, ~~library~~, ~~lawyer~~, firefighter, ~~hospital~~, ~~bakery~~, ~~factory~~, ~~secretary~~, ~~carpenter~~, garage, ~~farm~~, ~~waitress~~, ~~school~~, plumber

People	Places
nurse	Library
lawyer	Hospital
firefiter	baRery
secratary	faktory
carpender	garage
waitress	farm
Plumber	School

Directions: Make a list of *things to ride on*. See if you can think of eight answers.

1. rollercoaste   5. car
2. bus   6. Taxie
3. boat   7. firetruck
4. Plane   8. horse

Directions: Make a list of *writing tools*. Try to think of six.

1. craons   4. Computer
2. Pensles   5. pen
3. markers   6. inR

Same or Different Meanings

September 30, 2002

Directions: *Fast* and *quick* have the same meaning. Circle the pairs below that also have the same meaning.

Set I	Set II
1. (fast—quick)	1. thick—wide
2. bright—shiny	2. (save—keep)
3. bell—clock	3. buy—sell
4. (sad—unhappy)	4. (hill—mountain)
5. hide—seek	5. car—automobile
6. hungry—thirsty	6. (rush—hurry)
7. (object—thing)	7. shop—store
8. (look at—watch)	8. draw—paint
9. dog—cat	9. (happy—glad)
10. (want—desire)	10. sky—cloud

Directions: Can you think of another word with the same meaning? The first one is done for you.

over _____ above _____

build _____ constuct _____

angry _____ mad _____

hold _____ carry _____

clean _____ neat _____

Same or Different Meanings

October 1, 2002

Directions: The first word in each problem is underlined. Circle another word in the row that has the same meaning as the underlined word.

1. <u>grab</u>   throw   snatch   run   close   hang

2. <u>fight</u>   enemy   battle   sword   talk   soldier

3. <u>mend</u>   fix   buy   find   live   travel

4. <u>knock</u>   hit   window   door   plant   lock

5. <u>harm</u>   illness   accident   injury   help   charm

6. <u>bun</u>   fruit   soup   roll   cookie   beverage

7. <u>help</u>   cheer   fool   aid   hurt   tease

8. <u>push</u>   crush   pat   shove   bring   lift

9. <u>haul</u>   drag   store   clean   heap   distant

10. <u>scream</u>   music   yell   grip   bind

11. <u>dunk</u>   slide   trap   reach   dip   weigh

UNIT 1
WORD
MEANING

Opposites

The opposite of *empty* is *full;* the opposite of *black* is *white.*

Opposites are as different as they can be.

Empty is the least amount, *full* is the most amount;
black is the darkest color, *white* is the lightest color.

Directions: Give an opposite for each of the following words.

1. up ~~down~~ down ✓
2. stop ~~go~~ go ✓
3. yes ~~no~~ no ✓
4. wet ~~dry~~ dry ✓
5. thin ~~thick~~ thick ✓
6. work ~~rest~~ rest ✓
7. dark ~~light~~ light ✓
8. loud ~~soft~~ soft ✓
9. high ~~low~~ low ✓
10. cry ~~smile~~ frown lagh ✗
11. bumpy ~~smooth~~ smooth ✓
12. wild ~~calm~~ calm ✓
13. day ~~night~~ night ✓
14. break ~~bild~~ build/fix ✓
15. cold ~~warm~~ cool hot ✗
16. soft ~~hard~~ hard/loud ✓
17. light ~~darck~~ dark ✓
18. new ~~old~~ old ✓
19. little ~~big~~ big ✓
20. loose ~~tight~~ tight ✓

UNIT 1
WORD
MEANING

10

Opposites

Directions: In each row there is one word that is the opposite of the underlined word. Find this opposite. Circle it.

1. end   result   way   (start)   edge   item

2. yell   (whisper)   drink   weep   laugh   sigh

3. mean   crazy   angry   quiet   (kind)   lazy

4. sharp   pretty   nimble   boring   (dull)   brisk

5. melt   pester   listen   cover   guard   (freeze)

6. near   long   (far)   happy   tricky   alone

7. tall   wide   deep   thin   (short)   long

8. lost   soft   (found)   long   eager   wish

9. slow   quiet   near   glad   (quick)   sleepy

10. deep   useful   high   narrow   (shallow)   thick

11. easy   (hard)   bright   short   big   early

12. skinny   long   hungry   (fat)   afraid   tall

Word Relationships

1. nail, pencil, pin, tack

   They all have sharp points.

2. grass, leaf, pea, spinach

   They are all green.

3. baby carriage, wagon, car, bicycle

   They all have weels.

4. snake, worm, spaghetti, wire

   They are all long.

5. pie, face, globe, ring

   They are round.

6. telephone pole, fence post, broom handle, street sign

   They are all strait.

7. nail, screw, glue, tape

   They are all used to put stuff together.

8. lemonade, tea, soup, milkshake

   They are all liqueds.

UNIT 1
WORD
MEANING

Word Relationships: Jobs and Tools

Directions: Draw a line from each person to the thing he or she makes.

baker   music

carpenter   soup

author   lettuce

farmer   stool

cook   story

artist   bread

drummer   painting

Directions: Write down two tools used by these workers.

secretary _walky talky, lazer._

painter _canvis, paintbrush, paint._

gardener _hoe, shuvle, watercan._

house cleaner _cloth, duster, broom._

mechanic _screw, hamer_

cook _spacholay, knife, whiz._

Word Relationships: Time and Place

Directions: Some of the pairs of words below are related by time. Check the pairs of words that are about time.

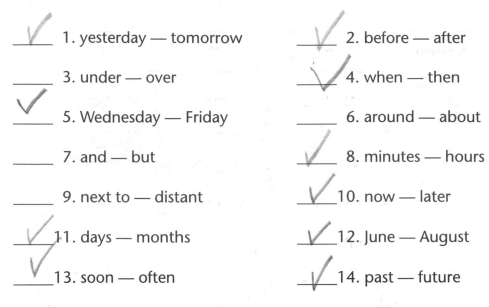

✓	1. yesterday — tomorrow	✓	2. before — after
___	3. under — over	✓	4. when — then
✓	5. Wednesday — Friday	___	6. around — about
___	7. and — but	✓	8. minutes — hours
___	9. next to — distant	✓	10. now — later
✓	11. days — months	✓	12. June — August
✓	13. soon — often	✓	14. past — future

Directions: The things below are found in particular places. Write a place where you are likely to find the word.

1. refrigerator _home_   2. Boston _Amerca_

3. couch _family room_   4. money _bank_

5. rake _groshe_   6. helicopter _air_

7. cow _farm_   8. bed _bedroom_

9. submarine _ocean_   10. chalkboard _classroom_

11. computer _libary_   12. toothbrush _bathroom_

13. carpet _school_   14. alarm clock _nighttable_

Word Play

Directions: Fill out the table below. For each group, think of a member of that group that starts with the letters A, B, C, and D. See how the first one has been done.

Group	A	B	C	D
Ways to Travel	Airplane	Bus	Cab	Delivery truck
Foods	apple	banand	cupcake	darkcholet
Animals	ant	bat	cat	dog
Names	Anna	britny	caroline	debra
Occupations	airline	busdriver	cabdriver	Dilivery man
Places	Africa	brizil	canida	Dolewere

Directions: The words in each problem below make a *pattern*. In number one, *red* is a color, *one* is a number, *blue* is a color, and *nine* is a number. To continue the pattern, in number one add a number after *black*. Add one word to the pattern in the other problems.

1. red, one, blue, nine, black, _____ eighteen _____

2. coat, apple, sweater, pear, shirt, _____ banana _____

3. hammer, house, ax, barn, pliers, _____ manchin _____

4. robin, lion, bluejay, horse, pigeon, _____ zebra _____

5. cup, table, bowl, desk, saucer, _____ shelf _____

6. March, Jason, October, Carly, August, _____ Alexa _____

UNIT 1
WORD
MEANING

Making Categories

Directions: In each problem a category has been started. After the two words, add two words to the category. The first one has been done for you.

1. sing, talk, _____whisper_____, _____cry_____

2. stick, branch, ___limb___, ___trunk___

3. saw, wrench, ___hammer___, ___screw___

4. carrot, potato, ___corn___, ___beans___

5. ring, bracelet, ___earring___, ___neckless___

6. cereal, bacon, ___Donut___, ___muffin___

7. subway, taxicab, ___bus___, ___car___

8. one, three, ___nine___, ___ten___

9. daisy, daffodil, ___lilly___, ___tulip___

10. ham, bologna, ___beef___, ___hot dog___

11. uncle, cousin, ___ant___, ___mom___

12. sneaker, boot, ___sandle___, ___party shoes___

13. grape, orange, ___apple___, ___chery___

14. pine, maple, ___oak___, ___flower___

Making Categories

Directions: Below are four words. Three belong to one group and one does not. Cross out the one that does not fit. Then add one that does belong to the group. The first problem has been done for you.

1. brown, ~~dark~~, black, purple ___blue___

2. lamp, candle, ~~table~~, lantern ___liter___

3. circle, rectangle, triangle, ~~coin~~ ___square___

4. rabbit, squirrel, ~~goldfish~~, chipmunk ___lion___

5. under, ~~better~~, over, inside ___outside___

6. ~~lift~~, run, walk, leap ___hop___

7. airplane, helicopter, jet, ~~tractor~~ ___glider___

8. toe, ear, ~~glasses~~, nose ___mouth___

9. baker, judge, ~~school~~, lawyer ___Actor___

10. pillow, ~~towel~~, blanket, bedspread ___matress___

11. peanuts, raisins, popcorn, ~~eggs~~ ___nuts___

12. ~~mouse~~, lion, elephant, hippopotamus ___Tiger___

13. some, lots, ~~box~~, plenty ___most___

Finding Categories

Directions: Circle the word in each list that does not belong; then explain how the other words are alike. The first one has been done for you.

1. puppy, kitten, calf, (horse,) piglet

   They are all baby animals.

2. hammer, screwdriver, (rake,) saw, wrench

   They are all tools.

3. toe, (sock,) finger, elbow, ear

   They are all body parts.

4. lunch, snack, breakfast, dinner, (bedtime)

   They are all meals.

5. teacher, coach, (library,) dentist, judge

   They all are jobs.

6. yellow, (light,) white, purple, brown

   They are all colers.

7. square, triangle, circle, diamond, (line)

   They all are shaps

8. aunt, uncle, cousin, (friend,) grandmother

   They all are relitives.

Finding Categories

Directions: Circle the word in each list that does not belong. Then write on the line how the other words are alike.

1. pancake, donut, cookie, (apple) pie

   They are all sweets.

2. speak, yell, whisper, talk, (write)

   They all ways too talk.

3. piano, drum, (pan,) guitar, flute

   They are all instermints

4. dime, (dollar,) quarter, nickel, penny

   they are all cence

5. pizza, hot dog, hamburger, (soda,) sandwich

   They all are food.

6. bang, burst, bump, crash, (bring)

   They are all nouises.

7. cup, glass, bowl, (spoon,) plate

   they are all places to put your food and drink.

8. book, comic, sign, magazine, (telephone call)

   They are all stuff you can read.

Analogies

We can understand how two things go together by seeing what they have in common. For example, we know that a butterfly and a moth go together because they both fly.

An **analogy** is a way to show how words go together. When you solve an analogy, you first look at how two words go together. Then you find other words that go together in the same way. You can do this by making a sentence that links the words.

First pair of words: top/bottom
A sentence: Top is the opposite of bottom.

Next, choose a word that creates the same relationship between a second pair of words.

Top is to bottom as over is to ___under___.

Top is the opposite of *bottom*. The word that creates the same relationship with *over* is the word *under*. *Under* is the opposite of *over*. The analogy reads:

Top is to bottom as over is to under.

Directions: Write down the way the first pair goes together. Then think of a word for the second pair that creates the same relationship. The first one has been done for you.

1. Monday is to Tuesday as June is to <u>July.</u>
   Monday <u>comes before Tuesday just as June comes before July.</u>

2. Ear is to head as thumb is to ___hand.___
   An ear ___is somthing you hear with.___
   _____

3. Suitcase is to clothes as wallet is to ___money.___
   A suitcase ___holds clothes.___
   _____

4. Apple is to fruit as carrot is to ___vegtuble.___
   An apple ___is a healthy fruit.___
   _____

5. Lace is to shoe as zipper is to ___jaket.___
   Lace ___helps to tie your shoe.___
   _____

Analogies

Directions: The first pair of word is related in some way. Find a word that makes the second pair go together in the same way as the first pair. Here is an example:

HONEY is to SWEET as LEMON is to _____sour_____

Honey tastes sweet just as lemon tastes sour. **Write *sour* on the line above. Now do the problems below in the same way.**

1. HAT is to HEAD as BOOT is to _____foot_____

2. POCKET is to PANTS as SLEEVE is to _____shirt_____

3. SPRING is to RAIN as WINTER is to _____snow_____

4. MOTHER is to AUNT as FATHER is to _____uncle_____

5. HUNGRY is to EAT as TIRED is to _____sleep_____

6. EARLY is to LATE as YOUNG is to _____old_____

7. AIRPLANE is to SKY as SUBMARINE is to _____water_____

8. TABLE is to EATING as DESK is to _____write_____

9. COACH is to TEAM as TEACHER is to _____class_____

10. PEANUT is to SHELL as BANANA is to _____peal_____

11. MUFFIN is to DONUT as LOLLIPOP is to _____Gum_____

12. LAMP is to LIGHT as FIREPLACE is to _____fire_____

13. PEPPER is to SALT as MUSTARD is to _____Kechup_____

14. FLOWER is to PETAL as BUTTERFLY is to _____wing_____

15. BOOK is to READ as MOVIE is to _____watch_____

16. CIRCUS is to CLOWN as ZOO is to _____lion_____

17. TREE is to BRANCH as HOUSE is to _____roof_____

18. INCH is to FOOT as MINUTE is to _____hour_____

19. RED is to STOP as GREEN is to _____go_____

20. PENCIL is to LEAD as PEN is to _____write_____

UNIT 1
WORD
MEANING

Analogies

Directions: Circle the letter of the pair of words that goes together in the same way as the pair in capital letters.

A 1. FOOTBALL is to FIELD as
   a. basketball is to court
   b. hockey is to stick

2. NURSE is to HOSPITAL as
   a. teacher is to school
   b. doctor is to illness

3. POUND is to WEIGHT as
   a. dime is to penny
   b. foot is to length

4. HAPPY is to GLAD as
   a. lazy is to funny
   b. angry is to mad

These problems are like the ones above except that there are four choices.

B 5. SHIRT is to COLLAR as
   a. collar is to dog
   b. sweater is to warm
   c. jacket is to sleeve
   d. skirt is to shoe

6. CHIMNEY is to BRICK as
   a. door is to wood
   b. floor is to rug
   c. wall is to room
   d. cement is to sand

7. LIGHT is to HEAVY as
   a. deep is to strong
   b. dark is to black
   c. ruler is to foot
   d. narrow is to wide

8. SOAP is to WASH as
   a. curtain is to pillow
   b. car is to wagon
   c. ink is to write
   d. wet is to dry

9. PEAR is to PEACH as
   a. apple is to red
   b. lemon is to lemonade
   c. fruit is to vegetable
   d. bean is to pea

10. CARPENTER is to HAMMER as
   a. gardener is to hoe
   b. bread is to baker
   c. nail is to glue
   d. pilot is to airport

11. HAND is to FOOT as
   a. arm is to leg
   b. shoulder is to shirt
   c. hat is to head
   d. hand is to clock

12. PIGEON is to BIRD as
   a. horse is to cow
   b. hawk is to sky
   c. egg is to nest
   d. poodle is to dog

13. RAPID is to FAST as
   a. new is to old
   b. ice is to cold
   c. hard is to stiff
   d. less is to more

14. FLY is to KITE as
   a. cook is to lemon
   b. ride is to bicycle
   c. ice is to skate
   d. bat is to ball

UNIT 1
WORD
MEANING

22

Analogies

Definition: Write down another pair of words that fit together in the same way.

1. CAT is to KITTEN as

   _____dog_____ is to _____puppy_____

2. START is to FINISH as

   _____gone_____ is to _____come_____

3. GROCER is to FOOD as

   _____water_____ is to _____drink_____

4. BOOK is to BOOKBAG as

   _____Tea_____ is to _____Tea cup_____

5. WHEEL is to BICYCLE as

   _____tail_____ is to _____cat_____

6. FATHER is to SON as

   _____Mother_____ is to _____doghter_____

7. CANOE is to LAKE as

   _____truck_____ is to _____road_____

UNIT 1
WORD
MEANING

Definitions

How do we define a word, such as *robin*? A definition tells us what a word means. If the word is a person, a place, or a thing, it tells us the group the word belongs to. For example, a robin is a bird. *Bird* is the group *robin* belongs to. Then a good definition gives us more information. We need these details so that we can see how the thing is different from other members of that same group. The robin is a bird that has a red breast and a gray-black head and back. These details help us see how the robin is different from other birds, such as a bluejay or a chickadee.

Directions: In the following definitions, underline the group that the person or thing belongs to. The first one has been done for you.

A 1. A (footlocker) is a small trunk used for storing your belongings.

2. A (cake) is a sweet food made from batter or dough.

3. A (taxicab) is an automobile that carries passengers for a fare.

4. A (detective) is a person who finds evidence to solve crimes.

5. (Corn) is a grain, usually a shade of yellow or white, that grows in kernels on large ears.

Directions: Underline the details that make the thing different from the other things that belong in the group. The first one has been done for you.

B 6. A (tent) is a shelter made of canvas stretched over a frame of poles, ropes, and pegs.

7. A (lynx) is a wild cat with thick, soft fur, a short tail, and pointed ears.

8. A (trombone) is a large brass instrument with a long bent tube that slides in and out to change tones.

9. A (raccoon) is a North American animal with a bushy, black-ringed tail.

10. A (grape) is a juicy fruit that grows in bunches on a vine.

UNIT 1
WORD
MEANING

Definitions

Directions: Define each word below. Tell the group that the word belongs to; then name details that show how it is different from other members of the group. The first one has been done for you.

1. A dragon is (GROUP) __an imaginary creature__

   (DETAILS) __has wings and claws and sometimes breathes fire.__

2. A mosquito is (GROUP) __a bug__

   (DETAILS) __it bites you to suck blood.__

3. A friend is (GROUP) __person__

   (DETAILS) __Someone who you play with alot.__

4. A raincoat is (GROUP) __jacket__

   (DETAILS) __it keeps the rain off you,__

5. A thumbtack is (GROUP) __Tack__

   (DETAILS) __It keeps stuff on bulutten bords.__

6. A giant is (GROUP) __person__

   (DETAILS) __that is big__

Definitions

A definition can also be a word or a short phrase.

Directions: Define the following words in this way. The first one has been done for you.

A 1. To shove is ___to push___

2. Happy means ___glad___

3. To jog is ___hop___

4. Delicious means ___yummy___

5. Angry means ___mad___

Directions: Below are definitions. Figure out the word that is defined. Write this word in the blank space. The first one has been done for you.

B 6. ___A boot___ is a shoe worn to protect the foot and some of the leg.

7. ___vet___ is a person who raises crops or animals as a business.

8. ___crawl___ is to move slowly on hands and knees.

9. ___bod___ is a hard substance formed by the freezing of water.

10. ___steal___ is to take something that belongs to another person without permission.

UNIT 1
WORD
MEANING

Definitions

Directions: Write a definition for each word. When you finish, look up the word in a dictionary. Compare your definition with the dictionary's definition. Make any changes you think are necessary.

1. A box is _Square_

2. An oven is _hot_

3. Slippery means _wet_

4. A doll is _Toy_

5. To wrestle means _fight_

6. To scribble means _to scugley lines_

UNIT 1
WORD
MEANING

Definitions

12\16

Directions: Read each definition below. If it is a complete definition, write *complete*. If it is an incomplete definition, write a better one.

1. A sandwich is something to eat for lunch. _complete_

2. To snore is to make noise through your nose or mouth as you sleep.
   complete

3. Toast is a breakfast food. _Toast is somthing you can eat for bredfast_

4. A nickel is a United States coin worth five cents. _complete_

5. A giraffe is a tall animal. _complete_

6. A crutch helps you walk. _a cruch helb you move_

7. A scissors is a tool with two connected blades used for cutting things like cloth or paper. _coplete_

UNIT 1
WORD
MEANING

28

Finding Different Meanings

Some words have more than one meaning. In the sentences below, the underlined words have a different meaning in each sentence.

Directions: Write a definition for each word. Make the definition fit the way the word is used in the sentence.

1. Marie took her <u>bat</u> and ball to the game.

   A long stick ar.

   Nathan saw a <u>bat</u> flying in the cave.

   A animal

2. Kerry <u>hit</u> the nail with the hammer.

   when you hith something to get in plase

   Joe got a <u>hit</u> in the last inning.

   when you hit a ball

3. After winter comes <u>spring</u>.

   a seson

   The wildcats can <u>spring</u> a long way.

   Jump

4. Kim wants to learn how to <u>box</u>.

   resling

   Gilberto can't find the <u>box</u> of napkins.

   a plase where you put stuf

5. Vanessa was <u>mean</u> to her brother.

   bad

   What does that word <u>mean</u>?

   the meanigg

UNIT 1
WORD
MEANING

Finding Different Meanings

Directions: Write a definition for each word. Make the definition fit the way the word is used in the sentence.

6. Don't <u>drop</u> that tray.

Dont let go of the tray

A <u>drop</u> of rain landed on her nose.

A bit of rain landed on her nose.

7. Sam <u>set</u> the table for dinner.

Sam got the table ready.

Christina has a <u>set</u> of silver bracelets.

Christina has a kit of braclets.

8. Can you <u>train</u> my dog to fetch a ball?

Can you teach my dog?

They took a <u>train</u> to Chicago.

They took a veicle to chicago.

9. On her <u>hand</u> she wore three rings.

On her skin she wore three rings.

<u>Hand</u> me a napkin, please.

Give me a napkin, please.

Finding Different Meanings

Directions: Put an X beside the best definition for the underlined word. The first one has been done for you.

1. Gary watched the rowboat <u>sink</u> out of sight.

   ____ a structure to hold running water in a kitchen

   _X_ to fall to the bottom of a lake, river, or ocean

2. Sergio ate the <u>rest</u> of the potato chips.

   _X_ the remainder

   ____ a period for relaxing

3. Giselle loved her silver <u>ring</u>.

   ____ the sound of a bell or telephone

   _X_ a piece of jewelry

4. The gymnast always seemed to <u>land</u> on her feet.

   _X_ end up

   ____ a body of solid earth

5. Melanie pushed with all her <u>might</u>

   ____ may, possibly will

   _X_ strength

6. Will you <u>hand</u> me the newspaper?

   _X_ pass

   ____ pointer on a clock

7. The clock's chimes began to <u>bug</u> Rachel.

   _X_ annoy

   ____ an insect

UNIT 1
WORD
MEANING

Finding Different Meanings

Directions: Put an X beside the definition that best fits the underlined word.

1. Ernie parked his car in <u>back</u> of the house.

   _X_ in the rear of

   ___ a football player

   ___ return

2. Kim's birthday is in the <u>fall</u>.

   ___ to drop

   _X_ autumn

   ___ raise up

3. How many sodas are <u>left</u>?

   _X_ remaining

   ___ the opposite of right

   ___ in the refrigerator

4. <u>Place</u> the dishes in the sink.

   ___ disturb

   ___ location

   _X_ put

5. Juan attached a <u>clip</u> to his key ring.

   ___ to cut off or cut out

   _X_ a fastening device

   ___ a gardening tool

Following Directions

Problem #1: Write the letters of each word in reverse order. The first one has been done for you. The letters of *tar* written in reverse order make the word *rat*.

tar __rat__   tap __pat__

spot __tops__   on __no__

pit __tip__   pan __nap__

part __trap__   peels __sleep__

pot __top__   yul __tug__

Now, make a sentence using four of the new words.

I pat my rat.

A nap is when you sleep.

Problem #2: How many words can you make from the letters of this word? Write them on the lines below.

submarine

rime. bar is bar are bus

sub are

in bus

Following Directions

Add a letter or letters to make a new word with each step. You will have to think about where the new letter should go to make a new word. The first one has been done for you.

Problem #1: Start with the word A: A

Add S: A   S

Add T: S   A   T

Add L: S   A   L   T

Problem #2: Start with the word I: I

Add N: I   n

Add K: K   i   n

Add S: S   K   i   n

Add L: S   l   i   n   k

Problem #3: Start with the word A: A

Add P: a   p

Add E: a   e   p

Add R: r   e   a   p

Add S: r   e   a   p   s

Problem #4: Start with the word ON: O   N

Add S: n   o   s

Add E: p   o   s   e

Add T: n   o   s   t   e

UNIT 2
SENTENCE MEANING

Introduction

A sentence is a group of words that go together. Sometimes a sentence tells about something that has happened; sometimes it tells a thought.

- When you change the order of the words in a sentence, you often change the meaning of the sentence. Look at this example.

    The farmer caught a rat in the trap.

    The rat caught a farmer in the trap.

Underline the two words that have been switched in this pair of sentences. How did switching the two words change the meaning of the sentence?

Change the meaning of this sentence by switching two words:

    The girl chased the pig down the road.

- Even a small word can affect the meaning of a sentence. Look at the small word that starts each sentence below. From these sentences only one of the small words makes a sentence that is *true*. Underline the sentence that is true.

    All children like to eat spinach.

    Some children like to eat spinach.

    No children like to eat spinach.

- Words must be in a certain order for a sentence to make sense. The sentence below is jumbled. Can you change the order of words so that the sentence makes sense? Write the words of the sentence in the right order on the line.

    Sentences you to to need understand think clearly.

    You need to think clearly to understand sentences.

Making a Sentence

A sentence tells a complete thought. *Uncle Joe* is not a sentence because it is not a complete thought. We want to know what Uncle Joe did or what happened to him. *Uncle Joe lost his wallet* <u>is</u> a complete thought.

Directions: Look at the groups of words below. They are not sentences. Add words to each group to make a whole sentence. Remember that a sentence tells a complete idea.

1. the broken window

   Somebody saw the broken window.

2. two tall cowboys

   Once there were two tall cowboys.

3. running down the field

   Sheila was running down the feild.

4. sent a letter to Santa Claus

   Leah sent a letter to santa.

5. at the zoo

   She had a cat at the zoo.

6. hates mashed potatoes

   She hates mashed patatos.

UNIT 2
SENTENCE
MEANING

37

Getting the Point

Sentences can be long. To understand what a long sentence means, we must figure out which of the words are the most important. For example, what is the main point of this sentence?

Many miles away from the earth, the astronaut fired a rocket, sending it into space.

There are many words in this sentence, but the main point is this: *the astronaut fired a rocket.*

Directions: In this exercise, you must find the most important idea of each sentence. Read each sentence. On the line, write the letter of the choice that tells the main point.

b 1. Behind the boat the hat was slowly sinking in the dark water.
   a. The hat was behind the boat.
   b. The hat was sinking in the water.
   c. The water was dark.

a 2. Dan hid his mother's birthday present under a stack of shirts in his closet.
   a. Dan hid his mother's birthday present.
   b. Dan's mother is having a birthday soon.
   c. He had a stack of shirts in his closet.

c 3. At the top of the mountain, Lucy took pictures of the beautiful view of the White Mountains.
   a. Lucy climbed the mountain.
   b. The view of the White Mountains was beautiful.
   c. Lucy took pictures of the view.

a 4. Nadine ate two bowls of the soup that Mr. Shiff had made for lunch.
   a. Mr. Shiff and Nadine had lunch together.
   b. Nadine ate two bowls of soup.
   c. Mr. Shiff had made the soup.

UNIT 2
SENTENCE
MEANING

Directions: On the line, write the letter of the choice that tells the main point of the sentence.

_a_ 1. On Saturday Wendy picked up her three dogs, who had stayed at the kennel for a week.
   a. Wendy picked up her dogs.
   b. The dogs had stayed at the kennel.
   c. The dogs were at the kennel for a week.

_b_ 2. The dump truck tipped over on the steep hill, so that garbage spilled into the street.
   a. The dump truck tipped over.
   b. Garbage spilled into the street.
   c. The dump truck was on a steep hill.

_c_ 3. At the edge of the pond the mother duck hid her eggs in a nest made of twigs.
   a. The mother duck was at the edge of the pond.
   b. The mother duck hid her eggs in a nest.
   c. The nest was made of twigs.

_b_ 4. At the end of Oak Street a fire burned down an old house that people called the haunted house.
   a. The house was at the end of Oak Street.
   b. A fire burned down the old house.
   c. People called it the haunted house.

_c_ 5. After the baseball game Gus couldn't find his car in the large parking lot.
   a. Gus went to a baseball game.
   b. The parking lot is large.
   c. Gus couldn't find his car in the parking lot.

UNIT 2
SENTENCE
MEANING

Getting the Point

Directions: Write an ending for each sentence. Your ending should show that you understand the idea of the rest of the sentence.

1. As he set the table, Terry put the napkins _near the salt._

2. After she washed the car, Beth used a rag to _dry the car,_

3. Under the couch in the living room Tom found _a old box._

4. At the end of the hockey game, the players _got to take a break._

5. When the telephone rang, Jane _answered it._

6. Mrs. Francis knew her camera was broken when _it did not flash._

Feb. 6, 2003

UNIT 2
SENTENCE
MEANING

Jumbled Sentences

Directions: The words in each of the sentences below are not in the right order; they are jumbled. Put the words in the right order.

1. Baked potato boy the ate the.

   The boy ated the baked patato.

2. The passed by the house truck fire.

   The truck passed by the fire house.

3. Apples the sisters like green.

   The sisters like green apples.

4. Father's on the chewed puppy my shoe.

   The fathers puppy chewed on my shoe.

5. Sold popcorn his my for friend club.

   My friend sold popcorn for his club.

6. Last Liza three the game in home runs hit.

   Last game Liza hit three home runs.

7. For to want you fish do dinner have?

   Do you want to have fish for dinner

8. Her jump friends likes Maya to with rope.

   Her friends like to Jump rope with Maya.

9. A the dog house children built.

   The children built a dog house.

10. Hay the to gave farmer horse the.

    The farmer gave hay to the horse.

11. Stolen his Joe's garage bicycle from was.

    Joe's bicycle was stolen from his garage.

12. Weekend I had finish homework to my the over.

    I had to finish homework Over the weekend.

13. Cousin brought his José dance the to.

    José Cousin brought his to the dance to.

14. Night one my uncle dinner cooked us for.

    One Night my Uncle cooked diner for us

15. Baseball game the to promised father to us take my.

    My father promiesed to take us to the baseball game

Over-Under

Directions: Look at the drawing of the heart, the star, the square, the triangle, and the circle. Then read the statements below. Write T next to each one that is true.

A _T_ 1. The circle is above the triangle.

___ 2. The triangle is over the square.

_T_ 3. The square is beside the star.

___ 4. The circle is below the square.

___ 5. The square is under the circle.

___ 6. The heart is inside the square.

_T_ 7. The circle is outside the heart.

_T_ 8. The square is between the triangle and the star.

Now add new shapes to the drawings.

B 9. Draw a star inside the square.

10. Draw a circle around the triangle.

11. Draw a heart between the triangle and the square.

12. Draw a square beside the circle with the heart inside.

UNIT 2
SENTENCE
MEANING

Over-Under

Directions: Underline the right word to finish each sentence. The first one has been done for you.

1. A cover is put (<u>over</u>, under) a pot.

2. A salad is made (on, <u>in</u>) a bowl.

3. A dog sleeps (<u>next to</u>, above) the kitten.

4. The students sat (<u>around</u>, inside) the table.

5. He borrowed a dollar (off, <u>from</u>) his sister.

6. The bridge was built (beyond, <u>over</u>) the river.

7. Alison shouldn't leave (<u>without</u>, with) permission.

8. Paul tucked his pencil (<u>behind</u>, between) his ear.

9. Sarah fell asleep (<u>during</u>, about) the movie.

10. Valerie looked (to, <u>through</u>) the book for the answer.

11. Return the library book (<u>within</u>, without) ten days.

12. The rider stood quietly (<u>beside</u>, beneath) his horse.

13. Linda lent her scarf (<u>to</u>, from) her sister.

UNIT 2
SENTENCE
MEANING

Small Words

Many small words can make a big difference in what a sentence means. For example, look at the way the meaning of the sentence changes when *under* is changed to *behind*.

The toothpaste is under the red towels.

The toothpaste is behind the red towels.

Which sentence says that the towels are on top of the toothpaste? Underline it. Circle the small word that helped you figure out the sentence to underline.

Directions: In the following problems, circle the letter of the sentence that answers the question.

1. Which sentence suggests that you will have to go past the fence to find the five chocolate eggs?
   a. Five chocolate eggs are hidden beside the white fence.
   b. Five chocolate eggs are hidden beyond the white fence.

2. Which sentence suggests that we must open the refrigerator to get the fruit?
   a. Ken put the fruit into the refrigerator.
   b. Ken put the fruit above the refrigerator.

3. Which sentence suggests that Mia's father is on one side of her, and her mother is on the other side?
   a. Mia took a seat between her parents.
   b. Mia took a seat next to her parents.

4. Which sentence suggests that Karen likes peanut butter and ketchup sandwiches?
   a. Karen never eats peanut butter and ketchup sandwiches.
   b. Karen often eats peanut butter and ketchup sandwiches.

5. Which sentence suggests that Jeff still has some comic books?
   a. Jeff gave Miriam all of his comic books.
   b. Jeff gave Miriam most of his comic books.

Small Words

B 1. Which sentence suggests that there are apples left in the bowl?
   A. The boys ate all of the apples in the bowl.
   B. The boys ate several of the apples in the bowl.

A 2. Which sentence says that Ed ate the cookies in bed?
   A. Ed ate the cookies after he climbed into bed.
   B. Ed ate the cookies before he climbed into bed.

B 3. Which sentence says that Marie sometimes delivers the newspapers
   during the week?
   A. Marie always delivers the newspapers on Sundays.
   B. Marie usually delivers the newspapers on Sundays.

A 4. Which sentence suggests that Justine could not ride her bicycle in
   the race?
   A. Before the race Justine's bicycle was stolen.
   B. After the race Justine's bicycle was stolen.

B 5. Which sentence says that more than one dog barked at my Halloween
   costume?
   A. None of the dogs barked at my Halloween costume.
   B. A few of the dogs barked at my Halloween costume.

UNIT 2
SENTENCE
MEANING

Word Order

Sometimes we can change the meaning of a sentence by changing the order of one or two words in the sentence. For example:

Only the cat ate the goldfish.

The only cat ate the goldfish.

The cat ate the only goldfish.

Sometimes the meaning does *not* change, even if the words are put in different order. For example:

In the garden was a snake.

A snake was in the garden.

Directions: For the pairs of sentences below, write *S* before the pairs that have the *same* meaning; write *D* before the pairs that have *different* meanings. The first one has been done for you.

D 1. Henry just gave me a dollar.
   Henry gave me just a dollar.

S 2. The boys found two kittens in the barn.
   In the barn the boys found two kittens.

D 3. Greg dropped soup in the peas.
   Greg dropped peas in the soup.

S 4. By the pond in the forest the bear slept.
   The bear slept by the pond in the forest.

S 5. She ran slowly down the narrow road.
   Slowly she ran down the narrow road.

D 6. The dog under the table bit my uncle.
   The dog bit my uncle under the table.

Directions: For the pairs of sentences below, write S before the pairs that have the *same* meaning; write *D* before the pairs that have *different* meanings. The first one has been done for you.

D 1. Only the gorilla eats rotten bananas.
   The gorilla eats only rotten bananas.

S 2. A few of the puppies tore apart the mittens.
   The puppies tore apart a few of the mittens.

D 3. Just Uncle Sam tried my fried fish soup.
   Uncle Sam just tried my fried fish soup.

S 4. Yesterday Ivan learned to juggle three balls.
   Ivan learned to juggle three balls yesterday.

D 5. The mechanic under the truck yelled loudly at the man.
   The mechanic yelled loudly at the man under the truck.

S 6. The airplane flew into the clouds.
   Into the clouds flew the airplane.

S 7. Finally Sandy scored a goal.
   Sandy finally scored a goal.

D 8. Fran added cheese to her ham sandwich.
   Fran added ham to her cheese sandwich.

D 9. Carmela only swept the cellar.
   Only Carmela swept the cellar.

S 10. Tim didn't want to go to the long, boring movie.
   Tim didn't want to go to the boring, long movie.

S 11. The man on the stage was singing.
   The man was singing on the stage.

D 12. Tom ate the last cookie.
   Tom ate the cookie last.

UNIT 2
SENTENCE
MEANING

Word Order

How many places can we put *only* in this sentence?

Fumio took his camera to the zoo.

The answer is four places. Here are the sentences:

Only *Fumio took his camera to the zoo.*

Fumio took his only *camera to the zoo.*

Fumio took his camera only *to the zoo.*

Fumio took his camera to the only *zoo.*

Notice how the meaning of the sentences changes as the word order changes.

Directions: How many places can you put *only* in the following sentence? Write the new sentences on the lines. Think about the different meanings of the sentences.

Ms. Abbott took five boys to the movie.

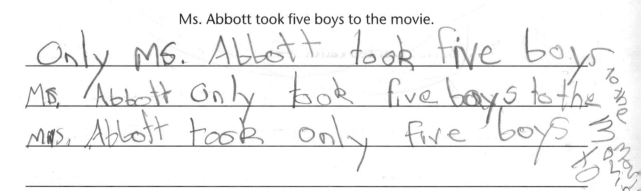

Only Ms. Abbott took five boys
Ms. Abbott only took five boys to the
Mrs. Abbott took only five boys

How many places can you put *just* in the following sentence? Write your sentences on the lines.

Grandmother left the house to go to the post office.

Just grand - mother left the
house to goto the post
grandmother Just left
the house to goto

Word Order

Directions: In the sentences below use all the words in the sentence to write it a new way. The first word or words have been given to you. If the new sentence has the same meaning, write *YES* beside the sentence; if it does not have the same meaning, write *NO*. The first one has been done for you.

__NO__ 1. Only Mary fed the turtle. __Mary fed the only turtle.__

yes 2. Under the rocks lived two snakes. Two snakes __Lived under a rock.__

No 3. Bill just ate the blueberry pie. Just __Bill ate a blue barry Pie.__

yes 4. The twins sat next to their uncle. Next to __their uncle the twins Sat.__

No 5. Ned planted carrot seeds in only one row. Only __Ned planted darott seeds in one row.__

yes 6. Mr. Rust warmed the milk to make cocoa. To make __cocoa Mr. Rust wamed the milk.__

yes 7. On the way to the store Bill lost his wallet. Bill __lost his wallet on the way to the store.__

Sentence Play

Directions: Read the sentence. Then label each of the numbered sentences below it _T_ for True, _F_ for False, or _CT_ for Can't Tell.

I. Neema's dog hid his bone under the front porch.

  _T_ 1. Neema has a dog.

  _CT_ 2. Neema has several pets.

  _T_ 3. Neema gave the dog a bone.

  _CT_ 4. The dog likes the bone.

  _CT_ 5. Neema lives in a house.

  _T_ 6. The house has a front porch.

  _CT_ 7. The house has a back porch.

  _CT_ 8. Neema's dog has hidden other bones.

II. Today the carpenters repaired the hole in the Smiths' roof.

  _F_ 1. There is just one carpenter.

  _T_ 2. There is more than one carpenter.

  _CT_ 3. The carpenters are good at their work.

  _T_ 4. Repair means to fix.

  _T_ 5. The roof is falling apart.

  _F_ 6. There is still a hole in the roof.

  _T_ 7. The Smiths live in a house with a roof.

  _T_ 8. Yesterday there was a hole in the Smiths' roof.

Directions: Read the sentence. Then label each of the numbered sentences below it _T_ for True, _F_ for False, or _CT_ for Can't Tell.

I. Nick just bought a dozen donuts for the soccer team.

   F   1. Nick has not bought the donuts yet.

   F   2. Nick bought the donuts a long time ago.

   T   3. Nick bought the donuts for the soccer team.

   CT   4. Nick likes all the team members.

   CT   5. The soccer players all like donuts.

   T   6. There are just twelve donuts.

   CT   7. The soccer team is having a game.

   CT   8. There are eleven players on the soccer team.

   CT   9. Just Nick bought donuts for the team.

II. Only Mrs. Lento, the science teacher, let Roxanne bring her hamster to class.

   CT   1. Roxanne is the only person in the class who has a hamster.

   F   2. The hamster does not belong to Roxanne.

   CT   3. There is just one science teacher in the school.

   F   4. Mrs. Lento won't let Roxanne bring her hamster to class.

   CT   5. Roxanne doesn't like school.

   CT   6. Roxanne has only one hamster.

Time Order

When we tell stories or talk about things that happen to us, we often use sentences that use **time order**. These kinds of sentences tell about events that happen before, after, or at the same time. Read these examples:

Andy ate the donuts after <u>he left the zoo</u>.

Jamie ate an <u>orange</u> before she read the magazine.

Two things happen in each sentence. Can you tell what happens first? In sentence 1, Andy left the zoo first. Then he ate the donuts. Underline "he left the zoo" to show that this happened first. Now do sentence 2. What happened first? Underline the part that happened first.

Directions: In each sentence below, two things happen. Underline the event that came first. The first one has been done for you.

Example: <u>Grandfather ate dinner</u> before he went bowling.

1. Mrs. Lewis sold her car to me <u>after she bought her motorcycle</u>.

2. Pat got her <u>pilot's license</u>, and then she flew her plane to Texas.

3. The Martínez family <u>picked up Aunt Estela</u> before they went to the opera.

4. Before the twins went on the class picnic, they <u>cleaned their room</u>.

5. After <u>we moved our furniture</u> to the new apartment, we cleaned the old one.

6. Mr. Chen <u>played tennis</u>, and then he took a nap on the couch.

7. Francisco took his <u>laundry</u> to the cleaners before he went to work.

Time Order

Directions: Two things happen in each sentence. Answer the question to show you understand the order of events.

1. Briana washed the car before her parents came home.

   Did her parents come home *before* or *after* she washed the car?

   _____After_____

2. When Jermain and Ed lifted the box, the bottom fell out of it.

   Did the bottom fall out *before* or *after* the boys lifted the box?

   _____after_____

3. Before Gail lost her English book, she had finished half of her assignment.

   Did she finish half her assignment *before* or *after* she lost the book?

   _____before_____

4. Mr. Taylor borrowed some flour, and then Mrs. Taylor borrowed some sugar.

   Did Mrs. Taylor borrow the sugar *before* or *after* her husband borrowed the flour?

   _____after_____

5. The dog barked while the fire alarm rang.

   Does one event happen before the other? If so, what happens first?

   _____No_____It happend at_____
   the same time.

UNIT 2
SENTENCE
MEANING

Cause-Effect

One thing sometimes makes another thing happen. For example, Alex slammed the front door. A picture fell off the wall, and the glass broke. The *cause* of the accident was slamming the door. The *effect* was that the picture fell, and the glass broke.

Here are some other examples of **cause-effect** sentences:

The rain storm caused our cellar to flood.

The spreading fire caused the animals of the forest to run away.

Directions: Each sentence below gives a *cause*, but not what happens as a result. Finish each sentence by writing down an *effect*. The first one has been done for you.

1. Because Tom lost his sneakers, ___he couldn't play___

   ___in the basketball game today.___

2. When lightning struck the tall tree, ___The tree burned down.___

3. Donna can't find her car keys, and so ___can't dive her car.___

4. Because Ping broke his leg, he can't ___Play with his friends.___

5. The refrigerator door was left open all night, and so ___the house got cold.___

Cause-Effect

Directions: In the following sentences decide whether one event really makes another happen. Write C for cause before each sentence in which one event makes another one happen. The first one has been done for you.

_C_ 1. When Jerome touched the hot iron, he burned his finger.

____ 2. Peter baked a cake, and then he went to the library.

_C_ 3. Since Frank ate the whole pizza, Steven did not get any.

_C_ 4. When my grandmother fell on the icy sidewalk, she broke her leg.

____ 5. After Mrs. Morelos bought the hat, she took a bus home.

____ 6. Before Juan went on vacation, he bought a camera.

_C_ 7. Because she slept late, Talia missed the bus to school.

____ 8. The twins played cards while their father made them sandwiches.

_C_ 9. When Sally left the water running, the bathtub overflowed.

_C_ 10. Tyrone stepped on broken glass, and so he cut his foot.

Cause-Effect

Directions: In the sentences below, label the cause sentences _C_ and the time order sentences _T_.

_T_ 1. Matthew drank his milk after he had eaten his peanut butter sandwich.

_C_ 2. Peanut butter sandwiches make my mouth feel very sticky.

_C_ 3. Susie's fingers look purple because she has been picking and sorting blueberries.

_T_ 4. Esteban made a pot of chicken noodle soup before he went skating.

_T_ 5. We ate the chocolate chip cookies just after Kevin took them from the oven.

_C_ 6. Winona put so much salt in the soup that we could barely swallow it.

_C_ 7. Oliver's loose tooth came out when Dad gave him a sticky candy to chew on.

_T_ 8. I'll pour the milk after you take the pizza from the oven.

_C_ 9. Since Henry left the ice cream sitting on the table all day, it melted and left a large, sticky puddle.

_T_ 10. Before the game started, the hockey players were nervous.

Comparison

We often talk about how two things are alike, or how they are different from each other. Showing likenesses or differences is called **comparison**. Here are two examples.

This sentence shows how two things are *alike*.

>   Both the radio and the television report news to us.

This sentence shows how two things are *different*.

>   A catfish is much larger than a goldfish.

Directions: In the exercise below, underline the things that are being compared. Write *L* before the sentence if it shows a *likeness*. Write *D* if it shows a *difference*. The first one has been done for you.

___D___ 1. My brother's cat is bigger than your dog.

_____ 2. John has twenty more baseball cards than Simone does.

_____ 3. Li-li's science report is just as long as yours.

_____ 4. Both Mr. Drummer and Mr. Tremble weigh more than 250 pounds.

_____ 5. Jeff puts more mustard on his hotdogs than you do.

_____ 6. Last fall Southwick School won fewer soccer games than Monroe School did.

_____ 7. That red sweater you are wearing is just like Pablo's.

_____ 8. Sheila's room is just as messy as her sister's.

_____ 9. Brian goes to work much earlier than Ayesha does.

_____ 10. Kelsey's phone bill is as big as Paula's.

UNIT 2
SENTENCE MEANING

Comparison

We use words like *larger* and *smaller* to make a **comparison** between two things: An apartment house is *larger* than a cottage; a tent is *smaller* than a house.

When we compare *three* or more things, we use the words *largest* and *smallest*. The questions below will show you how words like *smaller* and *smallest* are used. Think carefully about the items before you answer the question.

1. Is an elephant heavier or lighter than a bicycle? __Heavier__

2. Is a yardstick longer or shorter than a ruler? __Longer__

3. Is a nickel larger or smaller than a quarter? __Smaller__

4. Which is the smallest size—a dime, a nickel, or a quarter? __dime__

5. Which is the shortest time—a minute, a second, or an hour? __Second__

Directions: In the problem below, the words used to compare the coins are *more*, *fewer*, and *many*. Put a check beside each statement that is true.

Carl's uncle gave him six dimes. He put them in his wallet. Carl also has a quarter, three nickels, and two pennies in his wallet.

√ 1. Carl has more dimes than nickels in his wallet.

√ 2. Carl has fewer pennies than nickels in his wallet.

____ 3. Carl has more than fifteen coins in all.

√ 4. Carl has fewer than three quarters.

____ 5. Carl has just as many pennies as quarters in his wallet.

Comparison

Directions: Underline the things that are compared in each sentence. Write _L_ on the line if the comparison shows a likeness. Write _D_ on the line if the comparison shows a difference.

_L_ 1. Cake tastes just as sweet as pie does.

_D_ 2. Traveling by airplane is usually faster than traveling by train.

_D_ 3. Stools are less comfortable than chairs.

_L_ 4. Both eyeglasses and goggles protect your eyes.

_D_ 5. My father has more pairs of shoes than anyone else I know.

_L_ 6. Philip can run a mile just as fast as Terry can.

_L_ 7. An elephant is as heavy as some trucks.

_D_ 8. There is less milk in a quart than in a gallon.

_D_ 9. A trombone makes a deeper sound than a flute.

_L_ 10. Both butterflies and moths have large, flat wings.

_D_ 11. Maria wears longer skirts than I do.

Examples

One reason we give **examples** in sentences is to make it easier for people to understand exactly what we mean.

For example: *I hate crowded places*. You might not be sure what I mean by *crowded places* until I give you one or more examples. *Crowded places* might be movie theaters or baseball stadiums.

Give two examples for each group listed below.

1. farm animals ___Pig, Goat.___

2. boring jobs ___watching people dance, geting dresed.___

3. sweet snacks ___Ice cream, cokies.___

4. outdoor games ___Teniss, Golf.___

5. small pets ___Girbil, fish.___

Directions: The following sentences give one or two examples. Circle the group. Then underline the example or examples of that group. The first one has been done for you.

1. Isabelle likes to eat (sour fruits) like <u>lemons</u>.

2. Mrs. Nelson collects (tropical birds) such as <u>parrots</u> and <u>parakeets</u>.

3. Carlos hates (outdoor winter sports) like <u>skiing</u> or <u>skating</u>.

4. (Cooking) (fancy desserts) such as <u>Boston cream pie</u> is Mr. Ogata's hobby.

5. Ingrid must finish her (chores,) including taking out the <u>trash</u> and putting away her <u>laundry</u>.

Key Words

Read this sentence. Is it true?

All cars are red.

It is not true because *all* means that every car in the world is red, and we know that cars come in other colors. We can make the sentence true by changing the *key word*, *all*. Here is the new sentence:

Some cars are red.

Some and *all* are examples of **key words**. It is important to notice key words when deciding whether or not a sentence is true. Notice the key words in the sentences below. These sentences about cats are all true:

Some *cats are striped.*

No *cat is purple.*

Most *cats have long tails.*

All *cats have whiskers.*

Directions: Each of the following statements is false. Cross out the key word. In the blank at the end, write a different key word that would make the statement true. Choose from one of the four key words given above.

1. ~~All~~ teachers wear glasses. _Some_

2. ~~Most~~ mice have ears. _all_

3. ~~Some~~ snakes have legs. _No_

4. ~~No~~ squares have four sides. ~~all~~ _most_

5. ~~Most~~ cars have three wheels. _no_

UNIT **1**
SENTENCE
MEANING

Judging Sentences

Directions: Circle the number of each sentence that is *true*.

1. All leaves are green.

(2.) Most birds can fly.

(3.) Some fathers wear glasses.

4. No snow is cold.

(5.) All houses have walls.

(6.) Some cats catch mice.

7. No apples are green.

8. Most books have words.

9. All bread is white.

(10.) No cat can fly.

Directions: Circle the number of each sentence that is *false*.

1. Most gymnasts qualify for the Olympics.

(2.) Peanut butter is never eaten with jelly.

(3.) A cake often has icing on top.

4. Few birds are red.

5. All toast is made from bread.

(6.) Most pears are grown on apple trees.

7. No dinosaurs are alive today.

(8.) Few people own cars.

Judging Sentences

Directions: Add one of the following key words to each sentence to make it *true: all, some, most, few, no.*

1. _____ All _____ marbles are round.

2. _____ ~~so~~ most _____ chairs have four legs.

3. _____ No _____ hats are worn when we sleep.

4. _____ few _____ people eat grasshoppers.

5. _____ All _____ sweaters have sleeves.

6. _____ Some _____ trees have red leaves.

Directions: Add one of these key words to each sentence to make it a true statement: *always, usually, sometimes, often, never.*

1. Grass is _____ always _____ green.

2. Bicycles _____ Sometimes _____ have two wheels.

3. A flea is _____ never _____ as big as a dog.

4. A week _____ usualy _____ has seven days.

5. A quarter is _____ often _____ worth twenty-four cents.

Judging Sentences

Sometimes we cannot say whether a sentence is true or false. This might be because the sentence is an **opinion**. An opinion is someone's own feeling. Lou thinks broccoli tastes terrible; this is his opinion.

An opinion cannot be true or false. For example, is this sentence true or false?

All babies are cute.

We can't call this sentence true *or* false. Some people think babies are cute, and others don't. This is an opinion.

Directions: Read the sentences below. Label the opinions O.

_O_ 1. Most men who wear glasses are handsome.

____ 2. All children hate to eat spinach.

____ 3. No elephants are found on top of mountains.

____ 4. All ice cream is made of cream or milk.

_O_ 5. Orange juice always tastes better than grape juice.

_O_ 6. Most television shows are fun to watch.

____ 7. No nurse wears a uniform.

_O_ 8. Chocolate cakes are always delicious.

_O_ 9. Children always think clowns are funny.

____ 10. All triangles have three sides.

_O_ 11. Women with black hair always look nice in red clothes.

Same or Different Meaning

Directions: Read the two sentences in each problem. If the two sentences have the same meaning, label them _S_. If the two sentences have different meanings, label them _D_.

__D__ 1. John divided the cake into more than five pieces.
John divided the cake into as many as five pieces.

__D__ 2. The boy with the red hat sat down behind the bus driver.
The bus driver with the red hat sat in front of the boy.

__S__ 3. Sometimes the fire siren sounds at night.
At night sometimes the fire siren sounds.

__S__ 4. The living room is no larger than the kitchen.
The living room and the kitchen are about the same size.

__D__ 5. Dogs are usually bigger than cats.
Not all dogs are bigger than cats.

__S__ 6. Many children like to ride both escalators and elevators.
Children often ride escalators and elevators.

__D__ 7. The red square is larger than the yellow triangle.
The yellow triangle is as large as the red square.

__D__ 8. The doorbell rang before the dog barked.
The dog barked after the doorbell rang.

__S__ 9. The cookies are on the second shelf under the potato chips.
The cookies on the second shelf are under the potato chips.

__D__ 10. Tony had just one dollar in his wallet.
Just Tony had one dollar in his wallet.

Same or Different Meaning

Directions: In each problem, find the two sentences that have the same meaning. Put an X by these sentences.

1. _X_ Lamar can run just as fast as Cassie.

   _X_ Cassie and Lamar can run equally fast.

   ____ Cassie is not quite as fast a runner as Lamar.

2. _X_ Most cars have four wheels.

   ____ Every car ever made has four wheels.

   _X_ There are a few cars that do not have four wheels.

3. _X_ Several explorers have found the North Pole.

   _X_ The North Pole has been found by several explorers.

   ____ The North Pole is hard to get to.

4. _X_ The glass was dropped, and so it broke.

   ____ If the glass is dropped, it will break.

   _X_ The glass broke because it was dropped.

5. _X_ Most people wear boots on snowy days.

   _X_ On snowy days people usually wear boots.

   ____ Few boots are worn when it snows.

Problems and Practice

Directions: This exercise will give you practice writing different types of sentences. Each problem gives you the beginning of a sentence. Finish the sentences below.

1. **Time Order**

   After Casey _ate ketup she_ ✓

   felt quizy.

2. **Cause**

   Cristina broke her arm because _fell of a tree._

3. **Comparison**

   Anita has long red hair, but _Lizzy has short_

   curly har.

4. **Examples**

   The burglar took several pieces of Rebecca's jewelry _but_

   theu got cought.

Problems and Practice

Directions: In this exercise, figure out the type of sentence and label it: *T* **for time order,** *CE* **for cause-effect,** *C* **for comparison, or** *EX* **for examples.**

T   1. He gave me the comics after he had finished reading them.

EX   2. For breakfast Linda eats some fruit, such as grapes or pears.

C   3. My cousin carves wooden birds, just as his father does.

T   4. Marco stacked the blocks, and then his sister knocked them over.

EX   5. Herman eats many sweet snacks, such as donuts and cookies.

CE   6. Kenisha developed a rash because she is allergic to chocolate.

T   7. Ted reads sports stories, while Feng reads mysteries.

CE   8. Mary burned a hole in her blouse because the iron was too hot.

C   9. Frank is taller than Darrell.

T   10. Jan had dinner after she went to the movie.

CE   11. The sour milk made Tomás sick.

Following Directions

Follow this set of directions in the box.

1. If Wednesday is the day before Tuesday, put a W in the bottom left corner.

2. If summer comes after spring, put an S in the top right corner.

3. If an hour is longer than a day, put an H in the bottom right corner.

4. If a day is shorter than a week, put a P in the top left corner.

5. If tomorrow comes after today, put a T in the center of the box.

6. If November follows October, write O in the center of the top of the box.

7. Make a word using the letters in the box. Write it on the left side of the box. Can you make other words with the same letters? If you can, write them on the right side of the box.

P	O	S
Stop Pots	T	Tops
W		

Following Directions

Follow this set of directions in the box.

Write **TRUE** in the top left corner. Write **FALSE** in the top right corner. Now read each statement below. For every true statement, put an **O** under **TRUE**. For every false statement, put an **X** under **FALSE**.

a. Only dogs have tails.

b. All dogs have a nose.

c. Some dogs have fleas.

d. No people have dogs with fleas.

e. Some people's dogs have flea collars.

f. All flea collars have fleas.

g. No fleas have collars.

Count the number of **X**s and **O**s. Print your last name at the bottom of the column that has more.

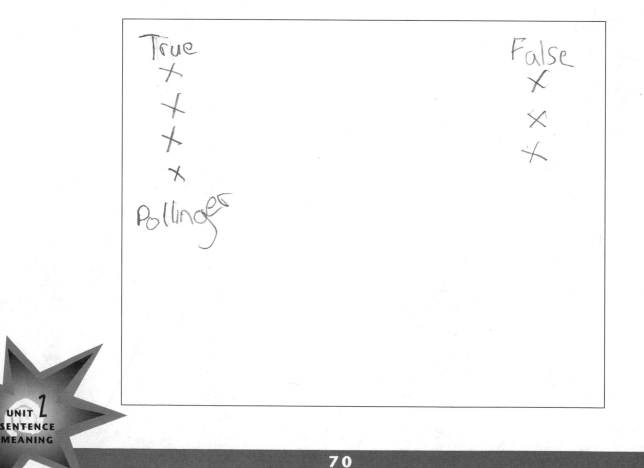

Introduction

A paragraph is a group of sentences that belong together. We can tell one paragraph from another because each new paragraph is indented or sometimes a blank space is left between paragraphs.

- Every paragraph has one main idea. When a new main idea is discussed, then a new paragraph should begin. Look at the group of sentences below. Two ideas are discussed, so there should be two paragraphs. Put an X where the second paragraph should start.

    Nancy has a bracelet collection. She spends all of her allowance on new bracelets. They come in all colors and many kinds of materials—wool, beads, plastic. When she wears them all at once, she has bracelets from her wrist to her elbow. Mary also collects old dolls. She has twenty-four dolls, many from faraway lands like Mexico and France. Her mother built shelves in her room so she could have a place to keep them all.

- The sentences in a paragraph should be about the same thing. Sometimes sentences tell about something that happened or describe something. In one of the paragraphs below, the sentences do not fit together well. Put an X on the line in front of this paragraph.

    _____ A.   Jason's brother bought a used car. He worked repairing the engine for many months. When the car was running well, he and Jason painted it a bright red. They named the car "Firecat," and they painted this name in black letters on both sides.

    __X__ B.   Terry and Andrea decided to go mountain climbing. They live on different streets. Andrea has a white car. White cars are easy to see when you drive at night.

Directions: Each paragraph below has two sentences that interfere with its unity. Cross out those sentences.

1. Mrs. Feliciano takes good care of her 1948 station wagon. She washes it once each month on a Sunday afternoon. Then she vacuums it, polishes the leather seats, and washes the windows. ~~Some people do not like to wash windows.~~ When she finishes, she usually checks the oil, the water, and the tires. ~~Mrs. Feliciano lives near the fire station.~~ Then she takes her husband and their dog for a drive in the country.

2. Miranda didn't have a kite, so she decided to make one for herself. She got a pattern from a book. Her mother helped her find some heavy plastic. ~~Plastic has many uses in homes and industry.~~ She painted a red and blue design on the plastic. Then she made a frame of light wood. She made a tail of scraps of fabric and tied a ball of string to the wooden frame of the kite. ~~The Chinese fly many kites on holidays.~~ Her last step was to see if the kite would fly. This she did in a field near her house.

UNIT 3
PARAGRAPH
MEANING

Unity

A paragraph is a group of sentences about one idea or topic. When all of the sentences are about the same idea, we say that the paragraph has **unity**.

Directions: The paragraphs below do *not* have unity. Each one contains two sentences that do not belong in the paragraph. Cross out these sentences.

1. Eric has been getting ready to build a porch on the back of his house. First, he measured the area. Then he drew up a plan. ~~In warm weather many people like to sit outside on a porch.~~ Eric then figured out how much wood he would need to build a porch. Next he borrowed his brother's truck to get the wood he needed from the lumber yard. He also checked to make sure he had all the tools and nails he needed. ~~His sister has a porch on her house.~~ Eric plans to start building the porch on Saturday, now that he has everything ready.

2. A group of friends have invented a game called "Hack," which is played with an old tennis ball. The ball is thrown quickly from person to person in a circle. If everyone catches the ball, the group has scored one "Hack." ~~Some people do not like to play games.~~ The purpose of the game is to see how many "Hacks" the four players can score without dropping the ball. ~~Tennis is a game played with racquets as well as with a ball.~~

Unity

Directions: Add one sentence to the end of each paragraph. Make sure the sentence fits the rest of the paragraph.

1. Aaron said he felt very tired. He asked Lauren if she would help him move the rocking chair on the porch. Together they pushed the chair into a patch of sunlight on the porch. Aaron sat down in it and started rocking. Lauren went into the house to get a blanket to put over Aaron's shoulders. ✓

   She came out with a blanket and a mug filled with hot cocs.

2. Warren wanted to buy an ice cream cone, but he had only a dime. He collected soda cans from his house and his aunt's garage. He took them in a large plastic bag to the grocery store. He got $1.20 for returning the cans. ✓

   But she still didn't have anof.

3. The garbage truck was backing up the driveway of the Kidder's house. The driver didn't seem to be watching where he was going.

   And he ran over a dog.

UNIT 3
PARAGRAPH
MEANING

Unity

Directions: Each paragraph below has been started but not finished. Add three or more sentences to each one. Make sure your sentences fit together so that the paragraph has unity.

1. If I could do anything I wanted on my birthday, I would like to

go to build a bear and go home
with an pinyata, and
A sleep over, and.

2. Sometimes we can learn a lot about a person by looking at the clothes he or she wears.

Example: Mrs. Pinkham has
a lot of jewlry so she
looks like she is a
buteatiful pirson.

Main Idea

Every paragraph has one **main idea**. In the following paragraph, the main idea is that hot dogs taste best at baseball games. Notice how every sentence helps build this idea.

> Eating hot dogs at home is nothing special. But at baseball games, hot dogs are great favorites. Hot dogs may taste better at a baseball stadium than at any other place. It doesn't seem to matter whether they are eaten with ketchup, with mustard, or with sauerkraut.

Directions: **When we are writing, we should start a new paragraph when the main idea changes. The exercise below is one paragraph, but it should be two paragraphs. Find the sentence that should start the second paragraph. Put an X before this sentence.**

> The Vincents are moving out of their apartment in the city. They have rented a van to move their furniture, and several friends will help them move their food, clothes, and pets. Their three children are going to stay with their grandparents while the move is taking place. The Vincents' new home is a farmhouse in the country. The house itself has many rooms. There is a small barn beside the house. Flower and vegetable gardens grow between the house and the barn. Behind the house are fields dotted with apple trees.

What is the main idea of the first paragraph? _What is going to happen_

What is the main idea of the second paragraph? _Their new house._

Main Idea

Directions: Each problem below looks like one paragraph, but it is really two paragraphs. Remember that each paragraph has one main idea. Find the sentence that starts the second paragraph. Put an X before this sentence.

1. The Parents Club holds a pet show every fall to raise money for the school. This year they want to help the sports program. They hope to raise $500 to buy new uniforms for the boys' and girls' soccer teams. X For many children the most popular part of the pet show is the Most Unusual Pet exhibit. Last year third prize was won by Henry Fenn's two hamsters, named Peanut Butter and Jelly. Second prize went to Nancy Pinter's raccoon, Bandit. First prize was won by Tamara Woo's garter snakes, Slip and Slide.

2. The fair was coming to town, and Jesse was eager to go because he had so much fun last year. He asked his parents to take him, but they were busy. Then he asked them if he could go with his cousin Dean. They told him he could go with Dean if he promised to be home by 8 o'clock. X On the day of the fair Jesse and Dean ran to the fairgrounds right after school. They went on many rides and played several games. Jesse ate a hot dog, some cotton candy, and a box of popcorn. Then when he went on the roller coaster, his stomach began to rumble unhappily. He felt sick, so he went home early.

Main Idea

Directions: Write the main idea of each paragraph on the lines below.

1. At one time people believed that the world was flat. They thought that if you traveled far enough, you would fall off the edge of the earth. Explorers eventually proved that the world is round. They sailed all the way around the earth and came back safely to report all that they had seen.

   It was about the explorers and others talking about the earth.

2. How is maple syrup made? First, sap is taken from a hole in a maple tree. A small pipe is used. A bucket is attached below it to catch the sap as it drips out. The sap is colorless and only slightly sweet. Then the sap is boiled for a long time. It becomes thicker and stronger in flavor. This is maple syrup.

   It was about what maple surup is made of.

UNIT 3
PARAGRAPH
MEANING

Topic Sentences

The sentence that gives the main idea of a paragraph is called the **topic sentence**. The topic sentence in the following paragraph is underlined.

<u>Trina is getting ready for soccer season.</u> She eats healthy food and gets a good night's sleep. She runs five miles almost every day. She also practices soccer with her friends.

A topic sentence is often the first sentence of a paragraph, so that you know what the paragraph is about from the beginning. Sometimes a topic sentence comes in the middle or the end of a paragraph.

Directions: Underline the topic sentence in each paragraph below.

1. <u>The county fair is held November of every year.</u> In addition to rides and the ring toss and cotton candy, the fair has a writing contest for every grade. Teachers at the local schools often enter their students' work. The first prize winners at each grade win free passes to the fair and unlimited ride coupons.

2. Judah borrowed his aunt's car to take a camping trip. <u>On his way back from the trip he got a flat tire.</u> He pulled over on the side of the road and changed the tire with the help of his friend. Then, as they were ten miles from home, a car ran a red light and dented the side of the car. Judah doesn't want to borrow another person's car again.

3. <u>Fernando thought he heard the sound of the key in the door.</u> Then the door creaked. The lights went on downstairs. Fernando heard footsteps on the stairs. At last his parents were home.

UNIT 3
PARAGRAPH
MEANING

Topic Sentences

Directions: Underline the topic sentence in each paragraph. Give each paragraph a title.

1. _Trying the chello_

Ann wants to take cello lessons, but she has to earn some money first. She will have to rent a cello. She also will have to pay for one month of lessons before she starts. She is going to earn the money she needs by babysitting on weekends.

2. _Searching Volcanos_

Jeff stopped at the library on the way home from school to take out books about volcanoes. He borrowed a pad of paper from his father. Then he searched through his desk and found three sharpened pencils. At last he had everything ready to start work on the paper for his science course.

3. _Packing for Vacation_

Pat does not like to pack the car when the family is going on a vacation. First, he knows that everyone is taking too many big suitcases and heavy items. He tells them they will not need things like a typewriter, but no one seems to listen. Second, he can never figure out the best way to pack the car. Usually, someone wants a bag that is at the very bottom of the pile. This means he ends up unloading and repacking the car at every stop.

Topic Sentences

Directions: Underline the topic sentence in each paragraph. Give each paragraph a title.

1. _____ Caching Mice _____

Pete has already caught all the mice in the old house. But now he is having a difficult time getting rid of the ants. First he set out ant traps that he bought at the store. Next he washed the cupboards and the floors. Then he made sure all of the food was in tightly-covered containers. However, he is still finding ants marching across the counter on their way to the sugar bowl.

2. _____ Calling _____

First, she called her brother's house. Then she tried Mrs. Martine's house. Last of all, she tried to reach the real estate office where her mother worked, even though it was after five o'clock. Lisette couldn't figure out where her mother had gone.

3. Going to The Pet Store

When the twins visit their grandmother, they ask her if she will take them to the pet store downtown. They like to play with the puppies. They pick one out for themselves, but of course they are not allowed to take it home. They spend time looking at the hamsters, the white mice, and even the snakes. They always hope they'll see Molly the minah bird.

Signal Words

Some words give the reader directions about what is coming up next. They are like traffic signals, which tell drivers whether they should stop or drive on. These words are called **signal words**. They help us follow the writer's thinking.

Signal words give different kinds of directions. Here are some examples:

Frank ate lunch. *Then* he went back to work. (*Then* shows the order in which things happened.)

Paul wanted to buy a radio. *But* he decided to save his money to buy a bicycle. (*But* shows a change of mind.)

That morning Nan had two problems. *First*, she needed a ride to the hockey game. *Second*, she had to find her lost skates. (*First* and *second* show a list of things.)

Directions: Complete the second sentence by writing a sentence that shows that you understand the meaning of the signal word.

1. Heather put flour into the bowl. *Next*, she _took a spoon_ _and mixed the flower._

2. Robin likes to chew gum. *But* _likes to suck lolly-_ _Pops better_

3. David must make his bed. *In addition*, _brush his_ _theeth._

Signal Words

Directions: Read the paragraph. Underline the four signal words. Under the paragraph, make a list of the events that the signal words point out.

Tommy made lunch for his mother the day she had a bad cold. <u>First,</u> he warmed a can of chicken noodle soup and made a peanut butter and jelly sandwich. <u>After this,</u> he put the soup and sandwich on a tray with a napkin and a spoon. <u>Then,</u> he picked some flowers from the garden to put on the tray. <u>Finally,</u> he carried the tray to her room.

First, _he warmed a can of_
chicken noodle soup

After this, _he put the soup and_
a sadwich with a tray with a spoon.

Then, _he picked some flowers_

Finally, _he carried the the tray_
to her room

Directions: Below is a paragraph that has been started but not finished. You are given the topic sentence and the signal words *some* and *other*. Finish the two sentences.

Different people watch television for different reasons. Some people _whath_
T.V. for wether.

Other people _whatch it for fun._

Signal Words

Read the paragraphs and follow the directions.

A   The waitress cleaned up the spilled soda quickly. First, she put a napkin over the spill to keep it from spreading. Then, she wiped the soda off the chairs. Next, she removed the tablecloth. Last of all, she put on a clean tablecloth and new place settings.

Directions: Circle the signal words. List the steps the waitress took. Use the signal words to help you.

1. _She put a napkin over a spill._
2. _She wiped the soda off._
3. _She removed the napkin._
4. _She put on a clean table cloth._

B   The class went to the museum to learn about dinosaurs and other early forms of life on earth. First, a guide showed the students the skeleton of a dinosaur. Then she showed them paintings by artists that showed the dinosaurs and other creatures as they roamed the land. Last of all, the guide told them about what happened to the dinosaurs. She wanted them to understand why no dinosaurs are alive today.

Directions: Circle the signal words. Then answer the questions.

1. Did the guide show them the skeleton before or after she showed them the paintings? _Before_

2. What was the last thing the guide did? _She told them what happened to Dinesors._

UNIT 3
PARAGRAPH
MEANING

Signal Words

Directions: Choose one of the signal words to complete each problem. Make sure the signal word connects the two sentences clearly. Here are the choices:

then, ~~next~~, ~~finally~~, ~~however~~, ~~and~~, ~~still~~, ~~so~~,
~~but~~, at the same time, instead, at last, ~~in addition~~

1. Stephanie can't drive a car. _____*So*_____ she takes a taxicab everywhere she goes.

2. Mr. Douglas is not a cheerful man. _____*but*_____ he likes to go to funny movies.

3. Tiffany poured charcoal into the grill. _____*And*_____ she lit a match.

4. Johnny waited for the bus for so long that he thought it would never come. _____*Finally*_____ it pulled up to the bus stop.

5. Lucy held the dog. _____*Next*_____ Vanessa combed the tangles from its hair.

6. Mike is tired. _____*in addition*_____ he refuses to go to bed.

7. Cindy was invited to go skiing. _____*however*_____ she had to borrow a ski jacket.

8. Mrs. Craig plays the piano. _____*Still*_____ she plays the violin.

UNIT 3
PARAGRAPH
MEANING

86

Time Order

Paragraphs that explain when things happen are called **time order** paragraphs. Usually a time order paragraph tells about things in the order in which they took place—what happened first, what happened next, and what happened last.

Signal words are often used to show the order of events. How many events happen in this paragraph? Count them. Underline the signal words so you can see the order.

Mrs. Tavares had a certain exercise routine. First, she did stretches. Next, she did a set of warm-up exercises. Then, she ran around the high school track six times, a distance of two miles. Last of all, she cooled down by walking home from the track.

Sometimes we use dates to show when things happen. For example: *I met Bettina in January, but she moved away in March.* We can also use words that show time order, such as *yesterday*, *tomorrow*, or *last week*.

Directions: Underline the words that show the time order in the following paragraphs.

1. Elizabeth is a high school freshman who has a busy schedule. Yesterday she had to study for her Spanish exam. She had to learn how to spell her first and last name in Spanish and count to a hundred. Today she has softball tryouts. She wants to get a spot on the team and hopes to play one of the bases. Tomorrow is Friday, which means she has to study for her history quiz.

2. On January 22, a tanker crossing the Atlantic Ocean ran into an ocean liner. Both sank to the bottom of the ocean. For three days afterward, the Coast Guard searched the area for signs of the two boats. Ten days later ten people who had been on the ocean liner were found. They were floating in a life boat many miles away, hungry and cold, but alive.

Time Order

Directions: The following events are not listed in the order in which they happened. Place them in the right order by numbering them from 1 to 5. The first sentence has been numbered.

_1_ Jan filled a bucket with soapy water and washed the car.

_5_ Finally, frustrated, she drove the soapy car to the car wash to finish the job she had started.

_2_ Then she found a very large rip in the hose.

_4_ She turned on the hose to rinse the car, but no water came out.

_3_ Next she searched the garage for another hose—with no luck.

Directions: In the following paragraph the events are not told in the order in which they happened. Read the paragraph; then answer the questions.

Joseph woke up in the hospital. His leg was in a cast and his head hurt. He tried to remember what had happened. He had been skiing down the mountain behind his father. He had hit an icy patch and lost control of his skis. He remembered sliding toward a large pine tree at the edge of the ski slope.

1. What happened first? _First he was skiing down the slope behind his_

2. What happened last? _He hit a large pine tree._

Time Order

Directions: The events below are not in the right order. Number them so that they are in the order in which they happened. The first problem has been started for you.

1. Science Fair

__3__ Partners have to come up with an idea for their projects by the end of the week.

__5__ Partners have three weeks to follow their plan and make their science fair projects.

__1__ Students in Mrs. Palmer's class are doing projects for the science fair.

__2__ They are assigned a partner that they will work with.

__4__ Once partners have thought of an idea for their project they have to write a plan for their project.

2. Rainy Days

__2__ He goes to his favorite place in the house, the couch.

__4__ He settles down for a day of reading.

__1__ Ross thinks that the best day to read is a rainy day.

__3__ He pulls the blanket from the couch over him.

3. Finding Pablo's Baseball

__4__ Terrance asked his father if they could use the ladder.

__1__ Steven and Terrance were playing with Pablo's baseball.

__2__ Steven hit the ball and it landed on the roof of Terrance's house.

__3__ The two of them knew they had to get the ball back for Pablo.

__5__ Steven climbed the ladder, got the ball, and threw it to Terrance.

UNIT 3
PARAGRAPH
MEANING

Steps in a Process

For some things we do every day, we follow steps in a certain order. A **process** is a way of doing things in steps, like tying your shoe or taking a bath.

Feeding a cat is a process. Here's one way it can be done.
Wash the cat's bowl.
Open the can of cat food.
Get a fork and scrape the food into the bowl.
Place the bowl on the floor where the cat usually eats.

Directions: **The following steps are for making lemonade, but they're not in the correct order. Place them in order by numbering the steps 1 to 4.**

4 Add ice and stir gently. Taste for sweetness.

2 Squeeze the juice of the lemons into the pitcher.

1 Set out a pitcher, six lemons, a quart of water, a half-cup of sugar, and a large spoon.

3 Add the sugar and the water. Stir briskly so that the sugar dissolves.

Directions: **Below is the beginning of a paragraph that describes the process of making a sandwich. Finish the paragraph by writing all the steps.**

Here is how I make a peanut butter and jelly sandwich. First, I put two pieces of bread on a plate. Then, I take my knife and spred some jelly on one of the slices of the bread. Next I take my knife and spred some Peanutbutter and spred it on the other slice. Then I put the two slices together

Steps in a Process

Directions: The steps are not in the right order. Number the steps to show the order in which they take place.

Writing a Letter

_5_ Put a stamp on the envelope.

_4_ Address the envelope.

_1_ Find a piece of paper and pen.

_2_ Write out your message.

_6_ Walk to the mailbox to put the letter in the mail.

_3_ Put the letter in the envelope.

Directions: Make a list of the steps for washing your hands or making a telephone call.

Pick up the phone.
Turn on the phone.
Dial the number.
Talk to the person.
Hang up.
Put the phone back.

Cause-Effect

When one thing makes another happen, we say that the two events are related by **cause and effect**. For example, Jean drops a plate, and it breaks. We would say that the *cause* is dropping the plate. The *effect* is that it breaks. In cause-effect paragraphs, we are told about the causes or the effects of things that happen.

Here is a paragraph that describes the cause of a girl's broken leg.

Janice went to school on Monday with a cast on her leg and crutches. All her friends gathered around her. They were curious to know what had happened to her. She said that her family had gone to a farm to pick apples. She had climbed a ladder and then climbed into an apple tree. At one point she reached far out to pick an apple. She lost her balance and fell from the tree.

What was the *cause* of Janice's broken leg? *Breaking her leg.*

Here is a paragraph that describes the effects of a book bag's tipping over.

Wendy's book bag was knocked over on the school bus. When she got home, she found that her notebook with the science report she had been working on was missing. She called the school bus company, but no one had seen a notebook with her name on it. Wendy had to start her report all over again the next day.

Wendy's book bag was knocked over. What happened as a result? *She lost her note book.*

Cause-Effect

Directions: Read the paragraph below. Then answer the questions.

On Sunday morning Mr. Thomas brought his newspaper out onto the porch to read. After he sat down, he couldn't find a pencil to do the crossword puzzle. He piled the newspaper on the table and went to get a pencil. While he was gone, a big gust of wind blew the newspaper across the yard. By the time he returned, a number of pages had blown into the street and were drifting between the passing cars. Mr. Thomas ran around the yard to collect all of the pages. His Sunday morning was not as peaceful as he had planned.

1. What *caused* Mr. Thomas's newspaper to blow away? _A gust of wind blue it away._

2. Mr. Thomas returned to find pages of newspaper blowing into the street. What did he do as a result?
He went out to collect the papers.

Write a cause-effect paragraph that continues after the sentence below.

Leon didn't have enough money to go to the circus, so he tried to sneak under the fence at the far end of the park. _But h a gard cought him._

_____

_____

Comparison

When we look at the ways in which things are the same or different, we are making a **comparison**. Some paragraphs of comparison show how two things are alike; some show how two things are different; others show how things are alike and how they're different. Here are some examples.

1. The two sisters do not look as if they belong to the same family. Kathy is tall and thin. She has dark brown hair and brown eyes. Jade is short. She has red hair and blue eyes.

Does this paragraph show how the two sisters are alike or how they are different? Explain.

This paragraph is about how two girls that so different but still sisters.

2. Mindy wants her two friends, Rachel and Kim, to meet each other because they have so many of the same interests. Both of them take a course in aerobic dancing, and both like cats. In addition, they both have large gardens and raise many different vegetables and flowers. Mindy thinks they would have a lot to talk about together.

Does this paragraph show how Rachel and Kim are alike or how they are different? Explain.

Mindy's friends are very alike.

Comparison

Directions: Read each paragraph. Then answer the questions that follow it.

1. The two cousins are both in the fifth grade, but the schools they go to are very different. Brian's school is in the country. He lives several miles from the school, so he rides a bus to get there. His class is very small—only fifteen students. Madeline goes to school in a city. She lives only three blocks away, so she walks to school. The school is very large, and there are thirty-five students in her class.

What two things are being compared? _Two schools_

Does the paragraph show likenesses or differences? _Different_

2. Linda thinks playing basketball is very much like playing volleyball. Team spirit is important in both sports. The members must work together to win. In addition, both are fast-moving games. Usually the score is close, so both games are exciting until the final whistle is blown.

What is being compared? _Two sports_

Does the paragraph give likenesses or differences? _Alike_

What are they? _Both sports involve alot of teamwork._

Examples

If someone asked you to give an example of a thing that jumps, you might say a kangaroo, a grasshopper, or a person. When we speak or write, we give **examples** to make an idea or group clear and concrete.

Directions: The subject of the paragraph that follows is "amusing books." Two examples are given to show what the author means by "amusing books."

Most students in Mr. Peterson's third grade class know that he likes amusing books, because he has read them so many. For example, this week he read *Horton Hatches an Egg*, by Dr. Seuss, a story about an elephant who sits on a bird's nest until the egg hatches. Last week he read *Curious George*, by Margaret Rey, a story about a monkey who gets himself into a lot of trouble.

What are the two examples? _Horton haches a eggs, Curious gorge_

Directions: In each paragraph below underline the examples.

1. Laura likes Saturdays because there are always so many things to do. For example, she likes to work on her collection of pictures of movie stars. She also likes to ride her bicycle and to help her mother in the workshop.

2. Danny and Ellen have many jobs to do around the classroom this week. For instance, Danny has to wash the blackboard and feed the goldfish and turtles. Ellen has to clap the erasers and water the lettuce and bean plants the class is growing.

Examples

Directions: Make a list of the examples used in each of the following paragraphs.

1. Mr. Jeffrey decided to clean out the refrigerator because something in it was smelly. He found several things that needed to be thrown away. There was a large piece of cheese with mold on top. There was an orange that had turned brown and squishy. There was a carton of cream that had turned sour. He realized that he should not have waited so long to clean the refrigerator.

   Cheese, Orenge, Cream,

2. Mr. and Mrs. Markel have accepted an invitation to spend the weekend at the beach with their friends. They aren't sure what they might do there, so they have loaded the car with all kinds of equipment. Mr. Markel put in golf clubs, tennis racquets, and a picnic basket. Mrs. Markel put in beach chairs, beach towels, hiking boots, a radio, and goggles for swimming.

   golf clubs, racquets, basket, chairs, towels, boot, radio, goggles

Writing Paragraphs

Directions: Finish writing each of the following paragraphs. Make sure that all your sentences are about the same main idea. Use signal words to connect your ideas.

Time Order Paragraph

Yesterday, a strange thing happened at our house. My mom said she had a strep thought. men, then my friend called saying she wouldn't be in school beacause she had strep thought!

Cause-Effect Paragraph

Last week I spilled a bottle of blue ink in my grandmother's living room. Because of that my grand mother was very mad at me.

Writing Paragraphs

Directions: Finish writing each of the following paragraphs. Make sure that all your sentences are about the same main idea. Use signal words to connect your ideas.

Comparison Paragraph

As pets, dogs are very different from cats. ~~Cats~~ Cats always ~~know~~ ~~lick~~ lick themselfes, dogs on the other hand licks you (humens). You can pick up cats but you cannot pick up dogs unless theor puppies.

Steps in a Process

Here is how I set the table for dinner. First, I put the tablle cloth on the tablle. Next I put on the plates. Then ~~~~ ~~puts~~ the silver weare.

Problems and Practice

Directions: Read the paragraph. Then answer the questions that follow.

Wrapping a present

Ellen was wrapping a present for her father. First, she picked out the wrapping paper and cut it so that it was just large enough to go around the box. Then, she placed the box on top of the paper. She folded the paper over the box and used a piece of tape to hold the paper together. Next, at one end, she put her hand close to the box and squeezed the paper into a small tight bunch. She tied a ribbon at this spot. Then she bunched up the paper at the other end and tied a ribbon there, too. Last of all, she wrote on the package, "Happy Birthday to Dad from Ellen."

1. What type of paragraph is this—cause-effect, comparison, or steps in a process? _steps in a process_

2. Circle the signal words.

3. On the line above the paragraph, write a title that shows the main idea of the paragraph.

4. Write a paragraph telling someone how to look up a friend's phone number in the phone book.

Leah opend a phone book to look up her friends phone number

Problems and Practice

Directions: Read the paragraph below. Then answer the questions that follow.

Run Free

Two weeks ago the Katz family got a dog, a mutt named Buster. For a week after that, people in the neighborhood went outside in the morning to find their garbage cans tipped over. Several of them decided Buster was the garbage thief, and they told Mrs. Katz that they were upset. The Katz family decided that Buster could no longer run free. They bought a long rope and kept him on this for a week. Then they built a fence around their backyard so that Buster could run around without causing trouble in the neighborhood.

1. This is a time order paragraph. How can you tell?

   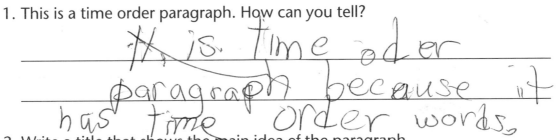

   It is time order paragraph because it has time order words.

2. Write a title that shows the main idea of the paragraph.

3. Let's say the garbage cans in the neighborhood are still being tipped over. What do you think will happen next? Write a paragraph about this.

   The people find out that it is another dog.

Problems and Practice

Directions: In each paragraph below, there are two sentences that do not fit in with the others. Cross out these sentences.

1. Mr. Hastings and his family are taking a train into the city. The children, Brian and Alexis, have never ridden on a train before. ~~Train tracks were built across our country many years ago.~~ The children think it is funny that you can sit so that you are riding backwards. They like the whistle that blows as they go through different towns. They also like the motion of the train. ~~Frank has a ten-speed bicycle.~~ Brian and Alexis are already asking their parents when they can take another train ride.

2. It is not difficult to find a good recipe to make a chocolate cake. However, the most important part of the cake is the chocolate. It takes good chocolate to make a rich and tasty cake. Good chocolate means pure chocolate, made from the seeds of a cacao tree. ~~Vanilla comes from the pods of the vanilla plant.~~ Don't use chocolate that has been mixed with other materials. And don't use chocolate that is called "chocolate-flavored." This may not have any real chocolate in it at all, and your cake will not taste much like chocolate either. ~~Butterscotch cakes are delicious also.~~

Problems and Practice

Directions: The paragraphs below need signal words or phrases to connect the sentences. In each blank space, write a signal word or phrase. Use one of the following:

then, next, at last, finally, however, but, in addition, first, second, still

1. Many people listen to the morning news. They want to know what is going on in the world. But, more important, they want to hear the weather report. Why is the weather so important? There are several reasons. ___first___, they want to know how to dress for the day. ___second___, they want to plan what they will do after they finish work or school. ___In addition___ the weather sets their mood. On sunny days people are more cheerful, while on rainy days they tend to be gloomy.

2. Joseph was trying to teach his brother Teddy how to ride a two-wheeler. He got Teddy to sit up in the seat while he held the bicycle. ___Then___ he told his brother to put his feet on the pedals and push. ___Next___ he ran along side the bicycle, holding Teddy upright. ___Finally___ he let go of the bicycle and watched Teddy ride on his own. Teddy fell over after a few yards, but he had had a good first lesson.

Following Directions

Directions: Read the paragraph below. Then complete the exercise that follows.

Jack, Mark, and Ned are brothers. Many people have trouble telling them apart. Here are some ways in which they are different. Jack's car is bigger than Mark's or Ned's. His car is yellow. Mark's car is blue, and so is Ned's. Mark's car has a big dent in the front fender though. Ned has a large dog, Moppy, who rides everywhere in his car with him. Jack has a dog, too, but his dog is never allowed to ride in his car. Mark doesn't have a dog, but he has a cat named Slick.

Label each of the following statements **T** for "true," **F** for "false," or **CT** for "can't tell."

__F__ 1. Mark has a dog named Moppy.

__F__ 2. Both Jack and Mark own yellow cars.

__T__ 3. Mark's car has a dent in the front fender.

__F__ 4. Jack takes his dog in the car with him.

__T__ 5. Slick is a cat, not a dog.

__T__ 6. Mark and Ned own blue cars.

__F__ 7. Jack's car is smaller than Mark's.

__T__ 8. Ned lets his dog ride in his car.

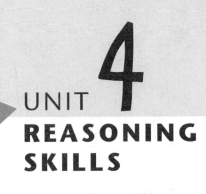

UNIT **4**

REASONING SKILLS

Introduction

Reasoning means figuring something out. Clear thinking can help us become good at school work and at solving problems and making decisions. Here are two reminders about reasoning:

• Good thinking starts by being ready and willing to think.

• Not every problem can be solved right away. Many problems take several tries. We can learn from our mistakes. Patience is an important part of good reasoning.

Here are two problems that will give you a chance to see what is meant by "reasoning."

1. Two boys and one girl are standing in line, waiting for the bus to arrive. Sandy is first. Sandy is not the girl. The second person is not a boy. The last person's name is Drew; the second person's name is Marty. Where is the girl standing, and what is her name? (Put labels on the picture to solve this problem.)

Sandy   Marty   Drew

Problem 2: All squirrels eat nuts. If Herman is a squirrel, will he eat nuts?

Yes

If I eat nuts, am I a squirrel? Not nessecarily

Fact and Opinion

A **fact** is a statement that you can prove is true. Here are some facts:

The sun rises in the east.

Bees make honey.

Australia is an island.

How could we prove that these facts are true? For the first one, we might go outside at sunrise with a compass. The compass will show that east is the direction of the rising sun, and so we can show this statement to be true.

For the second fact, we might ask an expert, such as a science teacher. Or we might look up "bees" or "honey" in an encyclopedia or a science book.

For the third fact, we might look at Australia on a globe or a map. We could also look up "Australia" in an encyclopedia or atlas.

Directions: Explain how you could show that each of the following is a fact.

1. A kangaroo carries her baby in a pouch.

   Look "kangaroo" up in an encyclopida

2. Babe Ruth was a famous baseball player.

   By finding a book about baseball/BabeR uth

3. Noodles are made from flour and eggs.

   A cook book

4. The carrot is the root of a plant.

   By looking up carrot on line.

Fact and Opinion

An **opinion** is an idea that a person or group of people believes. It is not like a fact. It cannot be shown to be true. Here are some opinions:

Cats make good pets.

Sausage can ruin a good pizza.

Lemonade tastes better than orange juice.

Some people believe that cats make good pets. Others don't. They don't like cats, and they don't think cats are good companions. There is no way to prove either of these beliefs to be true. That is why the first statement is an opinion. In the same way, some people like sausage on pizza, and others don't; some people like lemonade better than orange juice, and others don't.

Directions: Label each fact _F_ and each opinion _O_.

_O_ 1. Daisies are the prettiest flowers.

_F_ 2. Hawks eat mice and rabbits.

_O_ 3. Soccer is a more exciting sport than football.
(Fact)

_O_ 4. There should be more cartoons on television.

_F_ 5. The water in the ocean is salty.

_O_ 6. Learning to read is easy.

_F_ 7. Zebras are black and white.

_F_ 8. The earth is round.

_O_ 9. Boots are more comfortable than sandals.

_F_ 10. The sun warms the earth's surface.

Fact and Opinion

Here is a fact about the earth:

The earth is a planet that travels around the sun.

Here is an opinion about the earth:

The earth is a nice place to live.

Directions: Below you are given a fact about a topic. Write an opinion about that topic.

1. **Fact:** Snakes shed their skins several times a year.

   Opinion: Snakes ~~like cheese~~ make good pets.

2. **Fact:** A dictionary is a book that gives the spelling, meaning, and pronunciation of words.

   Opinion: Using a dictionary is easy.

3. **Fact:** A tornado is a funnel of rapidly moving air that destroys things in its path.

   Opinion: Tornadoes are cool.

4. **Fact:** A tricycle has three wheels.

   Opinion: Tricycle's weels are cool.

UNIT 4
REASONING SKILLS

Fact and Opinion

Directions: Write a sentence for each problem.

1. Write a *fact* about a car.

   Most cars are made of metal.

2. Write an *opinion* about airplanes.

   Airplanes are naesiating.

3. Write a *fact* about elephants.

   Elephants have ~~tusk~~ trunks.

4. Write an *opinion* about mice.

   Mice are cute.

5. Write an *opinion* about the city or town you live in.

   Holliston is a nice town.

6. Write a *fact* about your family.

   I have 4 people in my family.

7. Write an ~~opinion~~ fact about yourself.

   I am gorgeous

Fact and Opinion

Directions: In each paragraph there are several facts and opinions. Underline two facts. Put brackets [ ] around one opinion.

1. [Museums are fascinating places.] A museum is a place where people can go to see things that are being saved for all time. Different museums care for and display different kinds of things. Some show how people used to dress and live. Some show animals that are no longer alive. Some have works of art. Everyone should visit museums so that they can understand the history of the world.

2. Karen Smith was stopped by a police officer on Oak Street. The speed limit on Oak Street is 35 miles per hour. The officer's radar equipment showed that Karen was driving 45 miles per hour. [Karen feels that the speed limit on Oak Street should be 40 or 45 miles per hour.]

3. [Mr. Taylor thinks that a homemade apple pie has better flavor than a store-bought apple pie.] To test his belief, Mr. Taylor bought an apple pie at the store, and then he made an apple pie himself. He and Mrs. Taylor ate a piece of each pie. Mr. Taylor could not tell which pie was homemade.

UNIT 4
REASONING
SKILLS

Judging Opinions

We do not always agree with other people's opinions. Here is an example.

> Carl thinks that soda is bad for children. He thinks a law should be passed to stop factories from making soda. Some people do not agree with Carl. What is your opinion?

I don't agree with Carl.

Advertisements sometimes use opinions that sound like facts. Advertisers sell their products by getting us to believe their opinions. Here are examples of opinions, not facts.

> _Glow_ shampoo will make you a beautiful person.

> All smart people read the _Southwick Daily News_.

One way to judge opinions is to see whether or not they are reasonable. If the opinion is _not_ reasonable, we might not want to accept it. For example, would you accept this opinion?

> _An elephant makes a good pet. Every family should have an elephant._

We _know_ that an elephant is too large to fit in most people's houses. We would most likely call this a silly opinion.

Directions: Put an X by the opinions that do not seem reasonable to you.

_X_ 1. Children should be fed every other day.

_X_ 2. We can learn about wild animals by going to the (zoo.) captivity

___ 3. The moon is made of cheese. !!

_X_ 4. Round items can never be packed safely in square boxes.

_X_ 5. Drinking milk can hurt your teeth.

Judging Opinions

If you want people to accept an opinion of yours, give some reasons to support it. Some of your reasons should be facts. Here is an example:

Mary believes that white mice make good pets. Here are her reasons:

1. They are small. (fact)

2. They don't make noise. (fact)

3. They don't make a mess of her apartment. (fact)

4. They are soft and cute. (opinion)

She has given three facts and one opinion to support her belief. We don't need to accept her opinion, but we can see that it is reasonable.

Here is a different example:

Jeff believes that children should not have to go to school. Here are his reasons:

1. It is more fun to play at home. (opinion)

2. Children should choose what they want to do. (opinion)

3. School work isn't interesting. (opinion)

Jeff's opinion won't seem reasonable to most of us. This may be because he has used only opinions to support his idea.

Directions: List three reasons to support the following opinion. Try to give two reasons that are facts.

People should wear layers of warm clothes on very cold days.

1. It keeps you warm.
2. You won't be cold.
3. People won't look at you like a freak.

Judging Opinions

We might feel comfortable accepting an opinion that is backed up by facts. But what if we *don't know* any facts about the subject? Here is an example.

Ron's radio won't work. Three people give him an opinion about what is wrong with it. But Ron doesn't know anything about how a radio works or how to repair a broken radio. He can't tell if the opinions are backed up by fact. Now what should he do?

One answer is to think about whose opinion it is. It is probably a good idea to accept the opinion of a person who is an *expert* on that subject. For example, we are likely to believe a fisherman's opinions about fishing or a pilot's opinions about flying.

Directions: Below is a list of seven people and four opinions. For each of the opinions, choose the person you would be most likely to believe. Look for the person who is *an expert* in that area. Write this person's name on the line.

~~Edith the Electrician~~
~~Charlie the Car Salesperson~~
Sally the Science Teacher
Fred the Farmer
~~Barbara the Baker~~
~~Tom the Tailor~~
George the Grocer

1. "The style of men's suits today makes them look too casual."

    Tom the Tailor

2. "The wiring on that fan doesn't look safe."

    Edith the Electrician

3. "Blue cars are more popular than red cars."

    Charlie the Car Salesperson

4. "Whole wheat flour makes better bread than corn flour."

    Barbara the Baker

Relevant Information

To solve a problem you first must find the information you need. For example:

Larry's wife and three children have gone to watch him play in the town's Sunday softball game. Larry orders a hotdog for each of the children. How many hotdogs does he order?

To answer this question, you need to read the problem again to see how many children he has. This is the information you need to solve this problem. It is called **relevant information**. Here is another example:

Judy owns three dogs, two cats, and five goldfish. One of the dogs has brown ears. How many of Judy's dogs do not have brown ears?

Underline the information you need to solve the problem. What is the answer to the question?

2 dogs

Directions: Underline the information you need to solve the problem. Then write the answer to the question.

1. Beverly counted eight seagulls sitting on the roof of the building. Two had black wings, and the others had gray wings. Three flew away. How many seagulls are still sitting on the roof?

   5 seagulls

2. Mr. Herbert sold five electric brooms, three vacuum cleaners, and seven hair dryers last week. This week he sold four electric brooms, two vacuum cleaners, and an electric toothbrush. How many vacuum cleaners has he sold in the last two weeks?

   5 vacuum cleaners

3. Stan has invited six friends to a cookout. Two of his friends have called to say they cannot come. His father is going to cook steaks on the grill for everyone at the party. Stan's sister plays with a jazz band, and the band is going to play at the party. What are they having for dinner at Stan's party?

   steaks

Enough Information?

Does the problem give you the information you need to solve it? If so, answer the question. If there isn't enough information, write "Can't Tell" under the problem. "Can't Tell" shows that you need more information to solve the problem.

1. The orange sweater costs more than the yellow sweater or blue sweater. Which sweater costs the most?

   the orange sweater

2. Mr. Hart always does the dishes and takes the garbage out before he goes to work. Right before he leaves the house, he puts the dog in the backyard. His wife lets the dog in because she gets home before he does. She feeds the dog too. Does Mrs. Hart leave for work before or after Mr. Hart?

   Can't tell

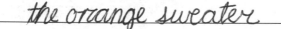

3. Mrs. Dennis planted a row of lettuce. She planted beans and carrots to the left of the lettuce. She planted tomatoes to the right of the lettuce. Are the carrots to the right or to the left of the tomatoes?

   left

4. In the apartment building, Brianna lives above Abe. Mira and Jude live next to Brianna. Who lives next to Abe?

   Can't tell

5. The barber shop opens at 8:00 A.M. The coffee shop opens at 7:00 A.M. The bookstore opens at the same time as the barber shop. If Mr. Thompson wants to go to the bookstore, what is the earliest time he can go?

   Cant tell

6. The bus stopped at the railroad station. Ten people got off. How many people are left on the bus?

   can't tell

Enough Information?

Directions: Put an X by each problem that *does not* give all of the information needed to solve it. Write down what is missing. Solve each problem that *does* give all the needed information. The first one has been done for you.

__X__ 1. Vanessa had twenty-eight bottles in her collection. She gave three bottles to her sister and several to her aunt. How many bottles does she have now? _____

We need to know how many bottles were given to the aunt.

__X__ 2. Eli put three eggs in each basket. How many eggs does he have altogether? _____

We need to knowsh how much she started with.

__X__ 3. Mr. Conrad's cat, Tucks, has lived with him for years. She was two years old when he got her. She has had four litters of kittens. She is good at catching mice around the house. How old is Tucks? _____

We need to know how long she lived with him.

__X__ 4. Guy jogs every morning. Today he ran three miles more than he usually runs. He ran as far as Terry's house and back. How far did he run today?

how long normally

__X__ 5. Helena went to the bank and the post office on her way to work. On her way home from work she stopped at the library to return some books. She also dropped her coat off at the cleaners. Did she go to the post office before or after she went to work? _____

what happened before work

__X__ 6. Tammy brought Mrs. Grant two watermelons and a box of strawberries to serve at the picnic. Now Mrs. Grant has three watermelons. How many watermelons did she have before Tammy arrived?

how much 1st?

UNIT 4
REASONING SKILLS

Making Decisions

When we want to make a decision we must think about what information we need. For example, the Gow family is thinking about getting a puppy. What kinds of information must this family have in order to make a good decision? They started a list of things they must discuss and decide on. Can you think of other things that are relevant? Add them to the list.

> the cost of the puppy
> where the puppy will sleep
> who is going to train the puppy

_____where will they get it?_____

_____

_____

Directions: Make a list of the kinds of information the following people must think about to make a good decision?

1. The Hummel family is thinking about taking a two-week vacation this spring, but they are worrying about Amy's missing school.

   ____–what work she will miss_____

   ____–the cost_____

   ____–can she make it up?_____

2. Elena wants Justine to volunteer to read to younger kids. Justine is not sure about whether or not to do this.

   ____–what it involves_____

   _____

   _____

Making Decisions

Directions: Karen's parents want to limit the amount of time she can watch television to one hour a day. Here are some reasons they might give. Circle the number of each reason that focuses on the problem.

1. You must eat a good dinner.

2. You need time to do your homework.

3. We want you to get exercise in the afternoons, and you have chores to do around the house, too.

4. We did not watch television when we were children.

5. Television shows are too violent.

6. The dog sleeps on the couch when you watch television.

Directions: Peter wants to buy a bicycle, but his parents are not happy about the idea. Here are some reasons Peter might give. Which ones focus on important and relevant matters? Circle the number of these reasons.

1. He hardly ever gets into trouble.

2. He will be able to get to his afternoon activities by himself.

3. His friends don't have bicycles.

4. He will get lots of exercise riding his bike.

5. He will be able to do his paper delivery route.

6. His friend Bobby got his bike when he was nine years old.

UNIT 4
REASONING
SKILLS

Inferences

To understand what is going on in the world around us we often make guesses about what we see and hear. These guesses are called **inferences**.

For example:

Brandy is looking out the kitchen window. This is what she sees:

Her brother Sam is limping toward the house.
Tears are flowing down his cheeks.
His bike is turned over in the driveway.

Brandy figures that Sam was riding his bike and that he must have fallen and hurt himself, but she didn't see him tip over. Brandy *inferred* that Sam got hurt on his bike.

Sometimes when people don't know all they need to know about something, they don't make good or complete inferences.

Here are two examples:

1. Three-year-old Kevin watched his mother spray an ant hill. She called the can she was using "bug stuff." Later on, when his mom was spraying perfume on herself he asked, "Are you putting bug stuff on, Mommy? Do you have ants on you?"

Kevin *inferred* that both kinds of spray were "bug stuff." He was not old enough yet to know that different sprays have different purposes.

2. Lisa saw her friend Amanda running down the road. She couldn't say why Amanda was running. There are many possible reasons why she was running.

Lisa could infer that:

Amanda wanted to get some exercise.
Amanda was looking for her dog.

What are some other inferences you can make about why Amanda was running?

She saw Mikko in the distance.

She was high.

Inferences

Remember that we make inferences about what we observe in the world around us. Here are two statements. One is an observation and one is an inference. Underline the inference.

Peter and Mandy are holding hands as they walk.

Peter and Mandy are good friends.

Directions: In each part of the following story, there are several observations and one inference. Find the inference in each part and underline it.

A Alfonzo put on his jacket and gloves and went out the front door. The wind was brisk. Gray clouds blew overhead. He figured it was going to snow.

B Alfonzo walked around the corner by the post office. He saw a gray station wagon in front of the building. He thought it looked like Mrs. Parker's car. Then he noticed that Mr. Lazaro was sitting in the driver's seat.

C Mr. Lazaro got out of the car. He pulled out a big package and slammed the car door. He seemed to be in a hurry to get to the post office. Just then Alfonzo noticed a sign on the front door that said, "MAIL YOUR CHRISTMAS PACKAGES TODAY."

UNIT 4
REASONING
SKILLS

Judging Inferences

Directions: Below are problems in which a person has made an inference. Decide whether the inference seems to be a good one. Answer each of the questions. The first one has been done for you.

1. Marcy knocks on Joe's door. No one answers. Marcy guesses that Joe is in the cellar and can't hear her, so she knocks again more loudly. What do you think of Marcy's inference?

   Marcy might be right, but there are many other possible reasons why Joe

   does not answer the door. He might not be home, for instance.

2. Phil has invited us over for a spaghetti dinner. He is carrying a big, covered pot to the table right now. We decide that this is the spaghetti he said he was making. Do you think we are right?

   _____

   _____

   _____

3. Mrs. Henry passes Mr. Romino walking toward the train station. She figures he is going on a trip. Would you agree with her?

   _____

   _____

   _____

4. Jenny pulls her boots out of the closet and puts them on. Her brother figures that she is going out. Do you think he is right?

   _____

   _____

   _____

UNIT 4
REASONING
SKILLS

Judging Inferences

Directions: Read the inference and answer the question that follows.

1. A candy bar costs forty cents at the vending machine. Charisse puts a quarter, a dime, and a nickel into the coin slot. However, when she presses the button to get her candy bar, a package of crackers comes out. Charisse guesses that the man who filled the vending machine must have put crackers in the candy bar slot. What do you think of her inference?

_____

_____

_____

2. Ted was looking out the front window. He saw a truck back up to the back door of the Phans' house. Two men got out and walked to the front door. Ted figured the Phans were moving. What do you think of this inference?

_____

_____

_____

3. Joel goes to his locker to get his sneakers for gym. They are not there. He figures that he must have put them in the wrong locker after gym on Friday. What do you think of his inference?

_____

_____

_____

Judging Inferences

Directions: The inference that is underlined is not a good one. Write a better inference.

1. Gerald's mother bought him a jeans jacket when he was eight. He didn't wear it much then. Now he is ten. He has found the jacket in his closet and tried it on. It is too tight for him. Gerald infers that <u>the jacket has shrunk</u>.

_____

_____

_____

2. In the middle of the baseball game Mrs. Watkins saw the team manager talk to the pitcher. Then a different pitcher came out to play in the game. She infers that <u>the first pitcher must feel sick</u>.

_____

_____

_____

3. Every day at the same time Mr. Lambert goes to the mailbox to pick up his mail. One day there is no mail there. He infers that <u>the mailman had forgotten to stop at his house</u>.

_____

_____

_____

UNIT 4
REASONING
SKILLS

Making Inferences

Directions: Read each situation below. Write one or more inferences you could make.

1. Mr. Douglas is standing in the front hall of his house. He has a dog's leash in his hand. He calls, "Come here, Sandy."

_____

_____

_____

_____

2. Martha said, "I am going to call Susie Morris." She dialed the telephone number. Ken Smith answered the phone.

_____

_____

_____

_____

3. Mr. Thomas took a flashlight from his pocket. He opened the front door very quietly and stepped inside.

_____

_____

_____

_____

UNIT 4
REASONING
SKILLS

Making Inferences

Directions: Read each situation below. Write one or more inferences you could make.

1. Ned opened the bag of lunch his mother had made for him. He was suprised to find that there was a ham sandwich inside. He was sure his mother had made him a peanut butter and jelly sandwich, because she always did.

_____

_____

_____

_____

2. Kate borrowed a mystery novel from Peter on Wednesday. On Thursday she returned the book and thanked him for lending it to her.

_____

_____

_____

_____

3. Betsy picked out a candy bar. She took some coins from her pocket and looked at them carefully. Then she put the coins back in her pocket. She put the candy bar back on the shelf.

_____

_____

_____

_____

Making Comparisons

Word problems often set up a comparison between two or more things. Here is an example:

> Sarah runs faster than Rayda. But Rayda runs faster than Diane. Which girl runs the fastest?

A good way to keep track of all the information is to make a diagram. The diagram should show the information compared (ranking it from most to least).

Here is a diagram that shows the information from each of the sentences:

fastest → slowest

Sarah
Rayda
Diane

The fastest runner is Sarah.

Directions: Fill in the diagram to solve each problem.

1. Ken had dinner at Hutch's Restaurant. He found that steak cost more than chicken. But lobster cost more than steak.

   Which one cost the *least*?

   _____

   most → least

2. For dessert Ken chose the chocolate cake because it was larger than the apple tart but smaller than the banana split.

   Which dessert was the largest?

   _____

   Which one was the smallest?

   _____

   largest → smallest

Making Comparisons

Directions: Solve the comparison problems below. Fill out the diagram to show the information given in the problem.

1. Planes travel faster than trains. Trains travel faster than cars. Which of these ways of traveling is the slowest?

_____

2. Joanne goes to bed later than Anita. Anita goes to bed earlier than Joanne but later than Steven. Who goes to bed the earliest?

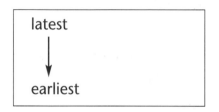

_____

3. An ice cream cone costs more than a soda. A candy bar costs less than a soda. Which costs the least?

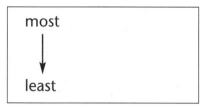

_____

4. John is taller than the twins, Marcella and Mike. Mike is a little taller than Mandy. Helen is shorter than Marcella. Who is the tallest?

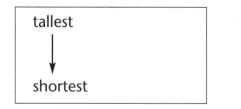

_____

Making Comparisons

Sometimes we aren't given enough information to solve a problem. Here is an example. Draw a diagram for this problem.

Bob is taller than Sam. Frank is not as tall as Bob. Who is the shortest man?

tallest

↓

shortest

We don't know whether Sam is shorter or taller than Frank. So the only answer we can give to the question is "can't tell."

Directions: Draw a diagram to solve each problem. If you don't have enough information to answer a question, write CT for "can't tell."

1. At the fair the Kimble family sold more candied apples than popcorn balls. They sold fewer candied apples than hotdogs.

   Which food did they sell the most of? _____

2. A farmer is raising three pigs. Boris is heavier than Pepper. Pepper is lighter than Enzo.

   Which pig is the heaviest? _____

   Which pig is the lightest? _____

UNIT 4
REASONING
SKILLS

Making Comparisons

Directions: Draw your own diagram to solve each problem.

1. Frank weighs less than Ramón. Louis weighs more than Ramón.

   Which man weighs the most? _____

   Which man weighs the least? _____

2. At the gift shop, marbles cost more than pencils, but marbles cost less than bracelets.

   Which item costs the most? _____

   Which item costs the least? _____

3. Rick can do the dinner dishes faster than Al. However, Ana is faster than Rick.

   Who is the fastest dishwasher? _____

   Who is the slowest? _____

For this last problem, you don't have enough information to answer *one* of the questions.

4. Jen's hair is a darker color than Dwayne's. Janine's hair is a lighter color than Jen's.

   Whose hair is the darkest? _____

   Whose hair is the lightest? _____

UNIT 4
REASONING
SKILLS

Syllogisms

A **syllogism** is a three-part problem that ends with a conclusion. Read the first two sentences of the problem below. Notice the conclusion.

> *All cats have whiskers.*
> *A Siamese is a kind of cat.*
> conclusion: *A Siamese cat has whiskers.*

In a syllogism, the first sentence is the general statement; the second sentence is a particular case; and the third sentence is a conclusion.

Here is another example:

general statement	*All elephants have a trunk.*
particular case	*Bumble is an elephant.*
conclusion	*Bumble has a trunk.*

We can also say the syllogism this way:

> *If all elephants have a trunk,*
> *and if Bumble is an elephant,*
> *then Bumble must have a trunk.*

Directions: Write the missing conclusion for the following syllogisms on the lines below.

1. If all birds have feathers,
   and a robin is a kind of bird,

   then _____

2. If all trees have roots,
   and an oak is a kind of tree,

   then _____

3. If every dog can bark,
   and a shepherd is a dog,

   then _____

Syllogisms

To draw a conclusion in a syllogism, there are two rules to follow:

1. In the general statement, the word "all" or the word "none" must be used. For example:

   All members of the class will take a spelling test today.

You can't draw a conclusion if the general statement uses the word "some." For example:

   Some members of the class will take a spelling test today
   You are a member of the class

Here you can't draw the conclusion that you will be taking the spelling test because you don't know if you are one of the members taking it.

2. The syllogism must say that the person or thing is a member of the particular case or group. In this example notice how the conclusion is unreasonable.

general statement	*All dogs have a tail.*
particular case	*Fluffy has a tail.*
conclusion	*Fluffy is a dog.*

Many kinds of animals have a tail. We can't say that Fluffy is a dog just because he has a tail. If the particular case said that Fluffy is a dog, we could draw a reasonable conclusion.

general statement	*All dogs have a tail.*
particular case	*Fluffy is a dog.*
conclusion	*Fluffy has a tail.*

Explain what's wrong with the reasoning in the following syllogism.

general statement	*Some dogs have black ears.*
particular case	*Butch is a dog.*
conclusion	*Butch has black ears.*

_____

_____

_____

Drawing Conclusions

Directions: Each reasoning problem below is given in two ways. One shows good reasoning. The other shows poor reasoning. Circle the letter before the one that shows good reasoning. Be ready to explain what is wrong with each problem with poor reasoning. The first one has been done for you.

1. a. If all monkeys like bananas, and I like bananas, then I am a monkey.

   (b.) If all monkeys like bananas, and Herb is a monkey, then Herb likes bananas.

2. a. If all boats float on water, and a canoe is a boat, then a canoe can float on water.

   b. If all boats float on water, and a leaf floats on water, then a leaf is really a kind of boat.

3. a. Some cars have tape players, and Jerry has a new car. Therefore, Jerry's new car will have a tape player in it.

   b. Some new cars have tape players. Jerry has a new car. His new car might or might not have a tape player in it.

4. a. Most television shows last for half an hour. "The Dance Contest" is a television show. It might last for half an hour, but we don't know for sure.

   b. Most television shows last for a half hour. "The Dance Contest" is a television show. It will last for a half hour.

5. a. No spiders have just four legs. This insect is a spider because it doesn't have four legs.

   b. No spiders have just four legs. Since the insect in that jar is a spider, it doesn't have four legs.

UNIT 4
REASONING
SKILLS

Drawing Conclusions

Directions: Think about the reasoning of each problem below. Label each conclusion *good* or *poor*. Be ready to explain your answers.

1. Some seals are kept in an aquarium.
   Flappy is a seal.

   Conclusion: Flappy must be kept in an aquarium. _____

2. No snakes have claws.
   Slip is a snake.

   Conclusion: Slip does not have claws. _____

3. All honey is made by bees.
   That is a can of wildflower honey.

   Conclusion: Wildflower honey must be made by bees. _____

4. All carrots are orange.
   That vegetable is orange.

   Conclusion: That vegetable must be a carrot. _____

5. Most children like popsicles.
   Betty is a child.

   Conclusion: Betty must like popsicles. _____

6. No bear can read.
   The grizzly is a kind of bear.

   Conclusion: A grizzly bear can not read. _____

7. All squirrels have fluffy tails.
   The animal in that cage is a squirrel.

   Conclusion: That animal must have a fluffy tail. _____

Drawing Conclusions

Directions: Write a conclusion for each syllogism.

1. If all flowers have petals,
   and a daisy is a flower,

   then_____.

2. If all fish have fins,
   and a guppy is a fish,

   then_____.

3. If all games have rules,
   and Scratch is a kind of game,

   then_____.

Directions: Now try to make up a few problems of your own. You are given the general statement.

1. If all cars have an engine,

   and _____,

   then_____.

2. If all fruits grow on bushes or trees,

   and _____,

   then_____.

Drawing Conclusions

We can't draw a good conclusion when we start with a false statement.

Here is an example of a conclusion based on a statement that is *not* true.

> All children like to make their beds.
> Sammy is a child.
> Therefore, Sammy likes to make his bed.

You can't say that all children like to make their beds, so the conclusion is not a good one.

Directions: Read each reasoning problem. The general statement is underlined. For *three* of the problems below, the general statement is *not true*. Circle the number of each of these problems.

1. <u>Every month is made up of thirty days.</u>
   March is a month.
   Therefore, there must be thirty days in March.

2. <u>All women are good athletes.</u>
   Sandy is a woman.
   Therefore, she must be a good athlete.

3. <u>All turtles have shells.</u>
   Boxer is a turtle.
   Therefore, Boxer must have a shell.

4. <u>All shoes have shoe laces.</u>
   Slippers are a kind of shoe.
   Therefore, slippers must have shoe laces.

5. <u>All butterflies have wide wings.</u>
   The monarch is a butterfly.
   Therefore, the monarch has wide wings.

Problems and Practice

Judging Inferences

Directions: Read the situation described below. Then write OK before each inference that is a good one.

A Tammy took out a piece of red paper and cut it into a rectangle. She folded the rectangle in half. Then she cut a heart out of white paper. She put glue in the center of the red paper and the white heart on top of that. She let it sit for a minute, then wrote her name on the inside. She put the red paper into an envelope and wrote "Bobby Eagan" on the outside of the envelope.

_____ 1. Tammy made a Christmas card.

_____ 2. Tammy made a Valentine card.

_____ 3. Bobby is Tammy's father.

_____ 4. Bobby is Tammy's neighbor.

_____ 5. The glue held the white heart to the red paper.

_____ 6. Tammy likes Bobby Eagan.

B Bobby got up early. He made orange juice. He cooked bacon and started making toast. Then he woke the other hikers. When he heard them getting up, he started the eggs.

_____ 1. Bobby knows how to cook bacon.

_____ 2. The other hikers don't like to cook.

_____ 3. Bobby is going hiking.

_____ 4. Bobby is cooking on a stove.

_____ 5. Bobby got up before eight o'clock.

_____ 6. The hikers are having bacon and eggs for breakfast.

UNIT 4
REASONING
SKILLS

Problems and Practice

Inferences

Directions: Write one or two inferences to explain each situation.

1. When Kerry took the laundry from the washing machine, she noticed that all of the white shirts and socks had turned light pink.

_____

_____

_____

_____

2. Peter went to get a drink at the water fountain in the hall at school. He turned on the water, but no water came out.

_____

_____

_____

_____

3. All spring the Rich family had been watching the birds who had built a nest in the tree outside their living room window. One morning Sally Rich noticed that a bright blue egg was on the ground under the nest. The shell was broken.

_____

_____

_____

_____

Problems and Practice

Making Comparisons

Directions: Make a diagram to work out the solution to each problem. If a question can not be answered, label it CT for "can't tell."

1. Mr. Vernon is shopping for a jacket that will fit him. The red jacket is larger than the blue one, but smaller than the yellow jacket.

   Which is the largest jacket? _____

   What color is the smallest jacket? _____

2. Lewis Marble's car cost more than Jerry Thorn's car did. However, Bob Friedman's car cost even less than Jerry's. Jerry's car is the smallest of the three.

   Which man spent the most money on his car? _____

   Which sentence is not needed to answer this question? Underline it.

3. Each family brought a steak to cook on the grill. The Tersells' steak is thicker than the Jenners' steak. It is also thicker than the di Mambro's steak.

   Which family brought the thinnest steak? _____

Problems and Practice

Directions: There are problems with the reasoning in each example below. Explain what the problem is. Write your answer on the lines.

Drawing Conclusions:

1. If most basketball players are tall, then that tall man must be a basketball player.

   _____

   _____

2. If all snow comes from clouds, then it is going to snow today because there are clouds in the sky.

   _____

   _____

Relevant Information:

1. Kevin's parents are going to paint his room. They want him to choose the color for his room. What must Kevin consider to make this decision?

   _____

   _____

2. Jeff has asked Kathy if she wants to buy his old skateboard. What things should she consider to make a good decision?

   _____

   _____

UNIT 4
REASONING
SKILLS